Antiquity was an age of superstition: today, we are in the age of science. Before reaching its present-day zenith, the modern, scientific age had to pass through three stages. The first was marked by the eradication of the superstitious mentality; the second saw the practical beginnings of scientific research; the third is the spectacular culmination of the scientific process in the second half of the twentieth century. The present volume examines the contribution made to the completion of the first two stages by Islam throughout its first millenium.

Other books by the same author

God Arises: The Evidence of God in Nature and in Science
Woman between Islam and Western Society
God-Oriented Life
Muhammad: The Prophet of Revolution
Islam As It Is
Islam: The Voice of Human Nature
Religion and Science
Indian Muslims: The Need For A Positive Outlook
Woman in Islamic Shariʿah
Tabligh Movement
Tazkirul Qurʾan
(Commentary of the Qurʾan in 2 volumes)
Allahu Akbar
(God is Great, in Urdu)
Al-Islam Yatahadda
(Modern Challenges to Islam, in Arabic)

ISLAM
Creator of the
Modern Age

MAULANA WAHIDUDDIN KHAN

THE ISLAMIC CENTRE, NEW DELHI

Translated by
Farida Khanam

Urdu version: *Islam: Daur-e-Jadeed ka Khaliq*

ISBN 81-85063-78-8

Al-Risala Books
The Islamic Centre
1, Nizamuddin West Market, Near DESU, New Delhi-110013
Tel. 4611128, 4611131
Fax 91-11-4697333

Distributed in U.K. by
IPCI: Islamic Vision
481, Coventry Road, Birmingham B10 0JS
Tel. 0121-773 0137, Fax: 0121-766 8577

Distributed in U.S.A. by
Maktaba Al-Risala
1439 Ocean Ave., 4C Brooklyn, New York NY 11230
Tel. 718-2583435

Printed in India

Contents

CONTENTS

Preface

The American astronaut, Neil Armstrong, was the first man to set foot on the moon after a four-day space voyage on July 20, 1969. On reaching his destination, he uttered these words which are now a part of history: "That's one small step for man, one giant leap for mankind."

Armstrong, along with his colleagues, Edwin Aldrin and Michael Collins, undertook this journey in a special rocket called Apollo II. In the final stage they boarded a lunar vehicle called Eagle in order to land on the surface of the moon.

These vehicles, the Apollo and the Eagle, were not— as some of the more fanciful among us might imagine—two magic, flying chariots, but scientifically designed machines made in accordance with our observation of the unchanging laws of nature. Their ability to traverse such immense distances in space is entirely due to man's correct application of his empirical knowledge.

These laws, the application of which would enable man to reach the moon, have existed throughout the universe since time immemorial, yet it took man centuries to discover them. Given the possibilities of nature, why did so many thousands of years have to elapse in the course of man's development before he felt ready to launch himself into space?

The answer to this is the prevalence of polytheism, a creed which looked upon things and creatures as deities, and encouraged their worship. In ancient times polytheism dominated the entire world. Man considered the moon a deity, just as he held all kinds of other inanimate objects to be gods. The moon, with its brilliant silvery light, inspired man to bow before it rather than try to conquer it. Holding the moon to be sacred was a major obstacle to even thinking of conquering it.

Then, for the first time, in the 7th century, the supremacy of polytheism was brought to an end by the Islamic revolution, which replaced it with monotheism, making it the dominant creed of the times. This revolution was initially brought about in Arabia. Later, it continued its onward journey through Asia and Africa to Europe. In more recent times, it has crossed the Atlantic to gain a foothold in America.

In the Muslim world this revolution was brought about through the influence of religion. The western world, with its own particular circumstances, began to develop this revolution along different lines, separating secular science from religion. Gradually, it was brought to its present culmination. The moon journey mentioned here is an obvious illustration.

Just as nationalization is an economic part of the

philosophic system evolved by Marx, similarly modern science is a part of Islamic revolution which has been separated from its whole.

The same is true of all the sciences which are now called natural sciences. The fields of these sciences had become forbidden territory because of the polytheistic view of the sanctity of all of nature's phenomena. It was the revolution of monotheism which opened the doors of research and investigation by displacing nature from its sacred pedestal.

Thus began a new era of freedom to investigate nature. The slow, thousand-year process of maturation finally culminated (towards the end at an ever-accelerating pace) in modern science and technology. Modern science is wholly the gift of the Islamic revolution — directly in its initial stages, and indirectly in its later stages.

This truth has been generally acknowledged in one way or another. A number of books which have come out in modern times, with titles like *The Scientific Achievement of the Arabs,* or *The Muslim Contribution to Civilization,* testify to its general acceptance.

Scholars are in agreement that modern industrial progress owes its existence to Arabo-Muslim influences. A. Humboldt writes: "It is the Arabs who should be regarded as the real founders of physics."[1]

Philip Hitti writes in his book, *History of the Arabs* (1970): "No people in the Middle Ages contributed to human progress so much as did the Arabians and the Arabic-speaking peoples."[2]

Historians have generally accepted that it was the science

which reached Europe through the Arabs (who were, of course, Muslims) which finally brought about the Renaissance (or the first awakening, to be more precise). Professor Hitti writes that Arabic translations of books available in different languages, as well as original works prepared by the Arabs in Arabic after the establishment of Bait al-Hikmah in Baghdad in 832, were translated into Latin. "This stream was re-diverted into Europe by the Arabs in Spain and Sicily whence it helped create the Renaissance of Europe."[3]

The question remains to be answered, however, as to what brought about this mentality in the Arabs in the first place, considering that they themselves had been submerged in the same backwardness which prevailed throughout the entire world of that time. There can be only one answer: the creed of monotheism was the cause of this mental and practical revolution. Other nations had polytheism, while the Arabs, after the advent of Islam, had come to be imbued with the spirit of monotheism. It was this difference which caused the divergence in their histories, one being shaped by the course of events, the other shaping history itself.

The aim of this book is to place a major historical event in its correct perspective, i.e. to attribute the crucial Arabo-Muslim contribution to modern science to Islam itself rather than give all the credit for it to a Muslim nation, which was formerly the practice. This is thus the explanation of a known event rather than the presentation of facts which were hitherto unknown.

This point can be illustrated by the manner in which India won its freedom in 1947. India's ability to liberate itself may be attributed to Gandhi and Nehru, but if we go into the matter in greater depth, we find it more proper to say that it was modern national and democratic ideas that helped India to win its freedom. This advent of a universal intellectual revolution, based on the principles of democracy and national freedom in modern times, actually paved the way for the rise of a Gandhi, or a Nehru, who was then in a position to launch a successful freedom movement. Had such a revolution in thinking not already taken place, the movements launched by our leaders would have had little chance of success.

The same is true of the subject under discussion. There is no doubt about it that the modern scientific revolution was set in motion by Arab Muslims. But the initial stimulus came from the new way of thinking which had been made possible by Islam. Logically, the history of science can no longer extol the achievements of just one nation, but must now show science in its true light as a gift of the religion which was sent by the Almighty for the guidance of all mankind for all eternity.

Henri Pirenne has acknowledged this as a historical fact: "Islam changed the face of the globe. The traditional order of history was overthrown."[4]

This book is a brief introduction to this aspect of the Islamic revolution. It was my intention to present an exhaustive study of the subject, but the work of collecting information was progressing too slowly. Finally, I felt that the pressure of my engagements would not permit me to prepare such a comprehensive work as originally intended

I decided, therefore, to publish in bookform whatever material was ready without delay.

If time and circumstances permit, more research will be done and more data added, Insha Allah. But if that plan does not fructify, I hope this first impression will be helpful to anyone else who wishes at some future date to embark on the preparation of the second impression.

WAHIDUDDIN KHAN
16 APRIL 1993

THE ISLAMIC CENTRE
C-29 NIZAMUDDIN WEST
NEW DELHI-110013

I

Islam: Creator of the Modern Age

The year was 1965 and I was on a visit to Lucknow. There I met a highly educated non-Muslim, who not only did not believe in religion, but who also considered religious discussions quite meaningless. In the course of the conversation, he put this question to me: "If Islam had never come into being, would there have been anything seriously lacking in world history?" I spontaneously replied, "Yes. There would have been the same shortcomings as existed before the advent of Islam." My answer silenced him. Then he had to concede that from the historical standpoint, all that would generally come under the heading of progress had not existed in the pre-Islamic era. All this had come to the world only after the emergence of Islam. He still had his doubts, however, as to how all progress was related to the historical event which is called Islam, or the Islamic revolution.

It is this historical question which this book endeavours to place in its proper perspective by making a thorough investigation of the connection between the Islamic revolution and modern developments. Even those aspects of the subject have been dealt with which have only an indirect bearing on the subject.

There can be no doubt that Islam, in essence, is the discovery of such divine guidance as shows man the path to eternal success in the Hereafter. Scientific and industrial developments may not be *directly* related to the aims and objectives of Islam, but it is nevertheless an indisputable fact that they are major offshoots of the Islamic revolution. Had the Islamic revolution never seen the light of day, scientific and industrial developments would also have remained unrealized.

The main purpose of a tree is to bear fruit. But, when it is fully grown, it also gives man shade. The same is the case with Islam. The main purpose of Islam is to open the door of divine guidance to human beings, so that they can come closer to their Lord. But Islam is complete truth. And when such truth reveals itself, it not only becomes the source of all blessings for mankind—directly as well as indirectly—but it also gives guidance which is of great practical utility.

FROM DARKNESS TO LIGHT

God created a perfect world. Then He created man in perfect form. Next He commanded man to live in the world and make use of everything he found in it. Man was told, moreover, that there was only one Creator who should be worshipped. Man was to worship this God alone, and none else besides Him.

But man went astray. He began to worship anything

which was visibly prominent, such as rivers, mountains, etc. He could not continue to make an invisible God the centre of his attention. Worse, his inclination towards visible gods went on increasing. Anything large and impressive was regarded either as a god, or as possessing divine attributes. This engendered, on the one hand, the concept of the sacredness of certain personalities and, on the other, the practice of nature worship, or pantheism.

This worship of some thing or person other than God finally developed into *shirk*, or polytheism. This *shirk* gradually came to dominate all aspects of belief and practice, finding its way into every household as a bearer of good omens and a nullifier of bad omens, thus becoming a part of all customs. Moreover, once belief in a divine king was added to all the other polytheistic beliefs, it became a necessary part of the political system.

This was the religion of the ancient world. Worship in those days was based wholly on *shirk*, to put it in religious terminology, or, in common parlance, superstition.

All the prophets in the past had come with the mission of rectifying this perversion. In all ages, throughout the history of man, they called for the renunciation of *shirk* and the adoption of monotheism. Over one hundred thousand prophets were said (according to one of the Traditions) to have come to the world from the time of Adam to the time of the Messiah (Christ). But man was not willing to give ear to what they had to say. The message of the prophet was thus confined only to the proclamation of truth; it could not go so far as to bring about a revolution based on this truth.

Rooting out *shirk,* or superstition, was not a purely religious undertaking. It had a bearing on all human concerns. The truth is that this all-pervasiveness of superstition served as a hurdle to all kinds of human development.

Placing nature upon a pedestal of sanctity had completely discouraged an investigation of it. Without such investigation, scientific and industrial progress was simply not possible. Progress towards the general acceptance of human equality was likewise barred by beliefs concerning the superiority or inferiority of a man's birth, which had grown out of a variety of baseless suppositions, all governed by superstition. The emergence of all those factors, which today add up to enlightenment and progress, had been rendered impossible by a complete absence of scientific vision. It was superstition which was responsible for delaying the birth of such an outlook by many centuries.

Efforts on the part of the prophets over a period of thousands of years had proved that any struggle which was confined to intellectual or missionary fields was not sufficient to extricate man from the grip of superstition. Even the governments of those times were founded upon superstitious beliefs. The interests of the rulers lay, therefore, in the perpetuation of the age of superstition, so that their subjects might continue to be swayed by the belief in the divine right of kings. (This was so that they should not question their right to rule.) That was why they used all their military and political might to suppress any attempts to put an end to polytheism and superstition by means of a missionary struggle.

ISLAM: CREATOR OF THE MODERN AGE

Now the question arose as to what strategy should be employed to break down the barriers raised by vested interests. This was the state of affairs when the final Prophet, Muhammad ﷺ came to the world in the sixth century A.D.

It was God's decree that he be a *da'i* (missionary) as well as a *mahi* (eradicator). He was entrusted by God with the mission of not only proclaiming to the world that superstitious beliefs were based on falsehood, but also of resorting to military action, if the need arose, to eliminate that system for all time.

Addressing the Prophet, the Qur'an observes:

> We have revealed to you this book so that, by the will of their Lord, you may lead men from darkness to light (14:1).

This same mission of leading men from darkness to light had been entrusted to all the prophets in turn. The sense, however, in which the Prophet of Islam was distinct from the others was that, in his case, God had decreed—since no Prophet was to come after him—that he should not just communicate the divine message to humanity and leave it at that, but that he should also take practical steps to change the entire existing state of affairs.

The prerequisites for putting this plan into action were all provided by God. Moreover, God also guaranteed that any shortcoming in worldly resources would be amply compensated for by special help from the angels.

This point has been made in the Hadith in different ways. One *hadith* in particular is quite direct in its wording: "I am the eradicator through whom God will obliterate unbelief." Thus the Prophet was not just a *da'i*, but also a *mahi*. He was the caller to the faith, but he had also to compel people to answer his call. The Qur'an clearly states that besides human beings, God's angels would also help him in accomplishing his mission.

This commandment of God was, indeed, realized through the Prophet, so that a whole new era could be ushered in.

THE NEGATIVE ROLE OF POLYTHEISM

According to the Qur'an, Adam was the first human being to exist on earth. God told him that his religion and that of subsequent generations would be monotheism. In this lay goodness in this world as well as in the Hereafter. For some generations people followed the true path, but soon the perversion set in. It was now that God began to send prophets to the world (2:213).

Noah was born in Iraq about three thousand years before Christ. He was chosen as God's messenger and entrusted with the task of reforming his people by showing them the right path. Then from Noah to the Messiah, the apostles were sent in succession. They made every effort to make people understand the error of their ways, but their listeners showed no willingness to be reformed (23:44).

The cause of this perversion lay in the inability of these people to see anything but externals, whereas monotheism demanded reverence for an unseen God. People unfortunately failed to find and worship this invisible God, and instead made visible objects their deities. The first form of religion had been monotheism, but the perversion that set in in later times resulted in the world going in the direction of polytheism.

Monotheism is the greatest truth. When man believes in one God alone, all his affairs are set right. When he forsakes this belief, all his affairs go awry. Monotheism provides the measure by which to judge the rise and fall of all human beings.

The Qur'an tells us:

'God is the Creator of all things. He is the Guardian. His are the keys of the heavens and the earth. Those that deny His revelations shall assuredly be lost. Say: would you bid me serve a god other than Allah, O ignorant men? It has already been revealed to you and those who have gone before you, that if you worshipped other gods besides Allah, your works would come to nothing and you would be among the losers. Therefore serve Allah and render thanks to Him.

They have not justly estimated the might of Allah. But on the day of Resurrection, He will hold the entire earth in His grasp and fold up the heavens in His right hand. Glory be to Him! Exalted be He above the partners they set up with Him (39:62-67).

The real extent of the harm done by deviation from monotheism will become apparent in the next life. Since monotheism is the reality of the universe, deviation from monotheism means, in effect, deviation from reality. The lives of those who deviate from reality will suffer from serious distortions not only in the next life, but also in the present world. This is the fact which is pointed out in the above verse.

The basic reason for this is that God-consciousness is ingrained in human nature. Man, as a result of his own natural urges, is forced to believe in God and surrender to Him. Man can refuse to believe in one God, but he cannot refuse his own nature. In consequence, those who do not believe in the Creator have to pay the price by believing (as one believes in God) in God's creatures. That is to say that, flying in the face of facts, they give to some creature or the other a status which they ought to give only to God.

The Creator and the Master of this universe is God. All true greatness belongs to Him alone. When man makes God his sole object of worship, he is acknowledging greatness in One who truly deserves such obeisance. By recognising that God is great, man stands face to face with the truth. As such, his life becomes a true life, free from all kinds of contradictions. His thinking and his actions both follow the right course. His being comes into harmony with the universe of facts. There is no contradiction between him and this universe.

Whereas when man takes something other than God to be great, when he accords to it a status which should be God's alone, the result is that his attitude becomes unreal. He becomes a thing displaced and disjointed which cannot be in accord with the universe of facts. His whole life, instead of taking the course of reality, takes the course of supposition.

Here is an example to illustrate this point. The Christians' belief in the Trinity made them suppose Christ, the son of Mary, to be God. Christ was, in reality, the son of Mary. But the Christians, exaggerating his importance, gave him the status of the son of God. They accorded to him the greatness of which only one God is deserving—He who is the creator of all human beings, including Christ.

As a result of this belief, they found themselves beset by great contradictions, one of which stemmed from their determination to view the solar system as a theological matter.

The ancient astronomer Ptolemy (90-168), who was born in Greece, carried out research in the time of Alexander the Great, writing a lengthy book in Latin, in which he advanced the theory that the earth was static and that the sun, moon and planets revolved around it. Thanks to the patronage of the Christians, this theory dominated people's minds until it was finally displaced in the 16th century by Copernicus.

As far as the Christians are concerned, the basic belief of Christianity is that of atonement, through which God ordained the salvation of the whole of humanity. The event of atonement, so central to this creed, relates not only to humanity but to the whole of the universe. Since the greatest single act of atonement, that of Christ's crucifixion (as atonement for the sins of humanity), took place on earth, the earth according to Christian theology, was assumed to be of the greatest importance in the universe and, therefore, its central point. This being so, Christians wholeheartedly supported Ptolemy's theory of geocentrism, giving it the status of a religious creed.

The Christians naturally opposed all attempts to prove

the truth of the heliocentric theory. It was only the research carried out by Copernicus, Galileo and Kepler which ultimately proved the falsity of this theory.[5]

According to the *Encyclopaedia Britannica* (1984), the scheme of salvation in Christian theology is a universal event. The act of atonement possesses a universal significance. It is related through human beings to animals. But the study of modern astronomy shows that the earth is no more than a small pebble in the vast sea of the universe. In view of this fact, the meaning of Christ himself has lost some of its impact, and the divine act of salvation appears merely as a tiny episode in the history of an insignificant little star.[5]

The Creator, Master, Planner—all are only one God. All greatness and power belong to Him alone. No one besides Him has any such greatness and power. As such, whenever any attempt is made to attach this greatness and sanctity to anyone else, such a concept comes into conflict with the whole universe, failing to fall into place in the universe as a whole.

This is why the concept of polytheism becomes an obstacle to human advancement, whereas the concept of monotheism opens the door to all kinds of progress for mankind.

THE CONCEPT OF ISLAM

According to the Qur'an, the message addressed to humanity by each of the prophets in turn did not vary. It remained in essence the same, namely, that there was only one God and that the people must worship Him alone.

What is the meaning of 'one God'? It means that, of all beings, He is the greatest, and should, therefore, be the object of man's awe. Indeed, if man ponders over God's creation, he will be thrilled to the very core of his being. Such an experience necessarily generates a sense of sanctity, this being attributable to something which is mysteriously great, which is above and beyond human imagination. This feeling finds expression in worship. That is when man surrenders himself to that Great Power. For him, Allah is the one and only God. There is no deity save Him, nor is there any partner in His godhead.

Belief in the true God is the source of all virtue: belief in false gods is the source of all evil.

THE ROOT CAUSE OF ALL EVIL

To believe something to be sacred when it is not so is the root of all evil. In religious terminology, this amounts to polytheism. Polytheism must be regarded as the greatest injustice, or *zulm*. *Zulm* in Arabic means, literally, the putting of something in the wrong place, in this case, the assigning of a value to something which does not merit it. *Shirk* (another Arabic word similar in meaning to *zulm*) is the greatest wrong, for it implies a reverence for things which are not, in reality, sacred or worthy of worship. It accords to non-gods the place which is the supreme prerogative of the one God.

The greatest harm in this iniquitous practice is that it changes man's focus of worship. He begins to revere such beings as are unworthy of reverence. The result is that man is deprived of the only support that he has in the universe. He is unable to have the sustenance of divine blessings. And one who is denied divine blessings in this world is denied them likewise in the next. Because no other power save that of God can give these blessings to man.

The loss to mankind affects not only the eternal life, but also our temporary stay here on earth. In ancient times man held many non-sacred things to be sacred, with the result that he continued to suffer the deprivation of God's succour for many centuries.

The concept of polytheism gave birth to many odd beliefs and spawned a whole series of superstitions. For instance, lightning was taken to be a god's fiery wand. When the sun or moon went into eclipse, it was supposed that some malign force was at work, or that some deity had been beset by the powers of darkness, and so on.

This polytheistic concept of sanctity proved highly advantageous to religious leaders, who developed the accompanying superstitions into a whole set of 'religious' beliefs. Through these, they began to exploit people by making them believe that they (the religious leaders) were intermediaries between God and man. They inculcated the idea that to please them was, indirectly, to please God.

The greatest benefit of all was reaped by the kings. Exploiting this mentality which had been conditioned in the people, they developed the concept of the god-king. In any society, the king is the richest and most powerful. He is distinguished, too, in many other respects from the common people. Taking advantage of this distinctive status, the kings instilled into the minds of the people that they were superior to common men, that they were, in fact, God's representatives on earth. Some said that they were a link between God and man. Others went further and pretended to be incarnations of God on earth. As such, they were supposed to possess supernatural powers. They managed, in consequence, to wield absolute power over their subjects.

The *Encyclopaedia Britannica* (1984) says in its article on sacred kingship:

> At one time, when religion was totally connected with the whole existence of the individual as well as that of the community and when kingdoms were in varying degrees connected with religious powers or religious institutions, there could be no kingdom that was not in some sense sacred.[6]

When the ancient concept of polytheism invested the rulers with a sacred status, not one, but two great evils found their way simultaneously into society. The evil that power brings had reached its zenith. As Lord Acton (1834-1902) put it, "Power corrupts and absolute power corrupts absolutely." If the public could not change rulers in a secular context in order to be rid of their oppression, how could they ever think of deposign those who ostensibly ruled as the viceregents of God on eargth, or who posed as His incarnations?

This political evil, which the French historian, Henri Pirenne, has termed 'imperial absolutism,' became a permanent obstacle in the way of all progress. It was only when Islam broke the power of these ancient empires that it became possible to unlock the doors to human progress.

Henri Pirenne's book, *History of Western Europe*, provides an informative study on this subject.

The gist of Henri Pirenne's thinking is that the ancient Roman Empire, which was spread over both sides of the Red Sea, had closed the doors to all human progress by imposing a strict curb on freedom of thought. Without this kind of absolute imperialism being brought to an end, freedom of thought could not have been achieved. When the human mind is shackled and cannot work in a free atmosphere, not even a beginning can be made to human progress.

The writer also includes Persia as being guilty of such imperial absolutism. And we must remember that these two empires held sway over a significantly large part of the inhabited world of the time. Under imperial rule, no one had the right to think independently if this ran counter to the official tenets of imperialism. This is why, after such a long period of intellectual suppression, no real beginning could be made on scientific enquiry. Scientific thought was simply not to be countenanced throughout the empires of Persia and Rome.

It was only when the Prophet and his companions broke these imperial powers—with as little bloodshed as possible—that free-thinking was legitimised, and the vast gates of progress were thrown open to humanity.

FREEDOM OF ENQUIRY

In his well-known book, *The Legacy of Islam* (1931),

Baron Carra de Vaux acknowledges the achievements of the Arabs, but nevertheless relegates them to the status of pupils of the Greeks. Bertrand Russell, too, in his *History of Western Philosophy*, sees the Arabs only as transmitters of Greek thought, i.e. that they brought Greek knowledge to Europe through their translations.

But this does not do justice to the academic attainments of the Arabs. It is true that the Arabs studied Greek literature and profited thereby. But what they transmitted to Europe was much more than they themselves had received from Greece. The truth is that the ideas which sparked off the Renaissance in Europe had not formed part of Greek thought. Had that been so, Europe's thinking would have been transformed much earlier. Then Europe would not have had to waste a thousand years before it could have its Renaissance.

It is well known that the progress made by the Greeks was mostly in the fields of art and philosophy. Their contribution to the field of science—with the exception of Archimedes' hydrostatics—was actually quite negligible.

It is an indisputable fact that for scientific enquiry and scientific progress, an atmosphere of intellectual freedom is absolutely essential. But such an atmosphere did not exist in any of the countries of ancient times, and neither did it exist in Greece. Socrates, for example, was forced to commit suicide by drinking hemlock as a punishment for his encouraging free enquiry among the youth of Athens. And Archimedes was struck down by a Roman soldier in 212 B.C. while pondering over geometrical problems in the sand.[7] According to Plutarch, in *The Ancient Customs of the Spartans*, the Spartans learned to read and write for purely practical reasons, and all other educational influences—books and treatises, as well as the discourses of learned men—were banned. The arts and philosophy flourished in democratic Athens, yet many artists and philosophers, among them Aeschylus, Euripides, Phidias, Socrates, and Aristotle were either exiled, imprisoned or executed, or they took flight.

Aeschylus was accused of violating the secrecy of the Eleusinian mysteries (rictions which had become part and parcel of Greek thought), His being put to death on the basis of this accusation is further proof of the fact that the atmosphere for scientific progress did not exist in ancient Greece.

The state of science prior to the modern, scientific age is well illustrated by the fate of Pope Sylvester II (Gerbert), who was renowned for his erudition. He was born in 945 in France and died in 1003. He was well versed in Greek and Latin, and was famous for his scholarly achievements in various fields.

Gerbert was taken to Spain in 967 by Count Borrell of Barcelona and remained there for three years. There he studied the sciences of the Arabs and was greatly impressed by them. When he came back from Spain, he brought with him several translations of these books and an astrolabe. When he began teaching Arab science, logic, mathematics, astronomy, etc., he faced stiff opposition. The Christians attributed his learning to magical arts learned in Spain, some to the devil's coaching. In such unfavourable circumstances, he finally died on May 12, 1003, in Rome.[8]

From the beginning of recorded history right up to the time of Islam, there had been no such concept as intellectual freedom. That is why we hear of only isolated instances of individuals who in ancient times, were given to scientific thinking. And scientific thinking could not spread beyond those individuals. For want of intellectual freedom, such thinking was nipped in the bud.

Islam, for the first time in history, separated religious knowledge from physical knowledge. The source of religious knowledge which came into general acceptance was divine revelation (the authentic version of which is preserved in the form of the Qur'an), while full freedom was given to enquiry into physical phenomena, so that individuals could arrive at their own conclusions independently.

The Sahih of Imam Muslim, the second most authentic book on Hadith, dating from the second century Hijrah, contains a chapter headed as follows: "Whatever the Prophet has said in matters of Shariʿah (religion) must be followed, but this does not apply to worldly affairs."[9]

In this chapter, Imam Muslim has recorded a tradition narrated by Musa ibn Talha on the authority of his father who said: "I was with the Prophet when he passed by some people who had climbed up to the top of some date palms. The Prophet enquired as to what they were doing. He was told that they were pollinating the trees in order to fertilize them by touching the male to the female. The Prophet said,

'I don't think this will benefit them.' When people learned of the Prophet's comment, they stopped the practice of pollination. The yield, however, was very low that year. When the Prophet came to know of this, he said, 'If they benefit from pollination, they should continue with this practice. I had only made a guess. It was an opinion. There is no need to follow my opinion in such matters. If, on the other hand, I say anything about God, it must be adhered to. Because I never say anything untrue when I am speaking of God."

The same story is told by 'Aishah, the Prophet's wife, and by Thabit and Anas, who were lifelong Companions of the Prophet. The Prophet finally told the date growers to adhere to their own methods, because "you know your world better."

According to this *hadith*, Islam separates religious matters from scientific research. In religious affairs, there has to be strict adherence to divine guidance. But in scientific research, the work must proceed according to human experience. This indeed marks the advent of the greatest revolution in the history of science.

THE ARAB IMPACT

It is true that in ancient times, there were certain individuals in different countries whose personal achievements in the field of science were considerable. However, due to lack of co-operation and other adverse circumstances, their findings did not gain currency either at home or abroad.

In his book, *The Arab Civilization,* Moseoleban, a French historian, explains that in ancient times, although many nations became sufficiently powerful to dominate others—Persia, Greece and Rome ruling over eastern countries at different times—they were unable to exert their cultural influence on these countries to any appreciable extent. Neither their religion, their language, their sciences, nor their industries could take root and flourish. Not only did Egypt hold to its own religion during the days of Roman rule, but the conquerors themselves adopted the religion and the architecture of the conquered. The buildings constructed in those periods were patterned on the architecture developed by the Pharaohs.

However, the goal that the Greeks, Persians and Romans were unable to achieve in Egypt was attained by the Arabs in a very short time and without resorting to the use of force. This was in spite of the obvious difficulties for Egypt in adopting the way of life of an alien nation and of adopting a new religion and a new language within the space of just one century, especially when it meant abandoning an ancient culture which dated back seven thousand years. The same influence was exerted by Arabs on African countries and on Syria and Iran. Islam spread rapidly among these peoples. Even in those countries where the Arabs never ruled, where they came only as merchants, Islam spread with great rapidity, China being one of the notable examples.

No similar instance is found in world history of such an influence being exerted by the conqueror on the conquered. Even those countries who merely had temporary contacts with the Arabs came to adopt their culture. More surprisingly, communities like the Turks and the Mughals, who conquered Muslims, not only accepted their religion and culture, but also became their staunchest supporters. Even till today, when the spirit of the Arab civilization is in decline right from the Atlantic Ocean to the Sindh River, and from the Mediterranean Sea to the deserts of Africa, one religion and one language are still in vogue—the religion and the language of the Prophet.[10]

Moseoleban states, moreover, that the Arab influence was as visible in western countries as it was in the East. From the Arabs, the West acquired a culture while, in the East, the Arab influence affected everything from religion and languages to the arts, crafts and sciences. In the West, religion, crafts and industries were not greatly affected. There was more influence on the arts and sciences.

Through the Arabs, monotheism, and a civilization born under its influence, spread everywhere. Its impact was felt in major parts of the inhabited world of the time. Thus an atmosphere and an environment were produced in which scientific research, leading to the conquest of nature's phenomena, could be freely and independently undertaken.

FOUR STEPS TO MODERNITY

In Islam, man has found true, unadulterated religion, in the sense that it has swept away all the artificial barriers between God and man for ever. Islam's sacred scriptures, the Qur'an and the *sunnah* (the practice of the Prophet to be followed) rise up like mighty towers to shed their light of guidance upon mankind for all eternity.

The Qur'an at various points stresses the fact that the religion sent by God to mankind in the shape of Islam is not only a source of guidance in the religious sense, but is also a blessing in many other ways (6:157). One very important way in which it was a blessing was that it brought human history out of the age of darkness, and caused it to enter into the age of light. This was a revolution in thought which unlocked the doors to innumerable worldly benefits. It is this second, worldly, aspect of the Islamic revolution which the well-known western historian, Henri Pirenne, describes in terms of Islam having "changed the face of the globe. The traditional order of history was overthrown."[11]

The present era, which we think of as modern and advanced—the age of science and industry, of freedom and equality—is a direct consequence of this aspect of the Islamic revolution which is called a blessing in the Qur'an. This period, like most other major historical developments, came about gradually, taking almost a thousand years to reach its culmination.

This gradual process may be broadly divided into four stages, the first three of which are directly connected with the Islamic revolution. The fourth stage is indirectly related.

1. The period of the Prophet, 610-632;
2. The period of the Pious Caliphs, 632-661;
3. The period of Umayyads and Abbasids, 661-1492 (including Spain);

4. The modern revolution brought about in Europe, which started in the 15th century after the crusades under the influence of Muslim civilization.

MODERN MAN

Till the beginning of the present century, it had been generally understood in the civilized world that the secret of progress was simply to lead man from the traditional to the modern. But, having reached his destination, man has again fallen prey to frustration. His feeling now is that to achieve real progress, man needs to have a more profound philosophical base from which to launch himself. Various articles on this issue have recently been published under such headings as 'Shallow are the Roots,' etc.

Now, writers in the western world are taking up this issue. One of the more prominent is William E. Connolly, who authored *Political Theory and Modernity.*

Professor Connolly writes:

> The whole project of modernity, despite its stunning success, is highly problematic. This is because all attempts to fill the place which God was forced to vacate at the start of the project—with reason, with the general will, the dialectic of history — have been of no avail, and each has ended up in one kind of nihilism or another.[12]

Before the advent of Islam, the world was in the grip of polytheism. Men's minds were ruled by polytheistic thoughts. The creature had taken the place of the Creator. Man worshipped innumerable gods. As a result, his whole way of thinking had gone awry, and the door to all progress remained locked.

Then Islam came to the world. Its main objective was to put an end to polytheism and to give monotheism the place of predominance. After great sacrifice on the part of the Prophet and his companions, polytheism was indeed displaced forever, giving monotheism the ascendancy. The effect of this revolution was so far-reaching, that monotheism remained in full force for almost a thousand years. Then came the emergence of modern industrial civilization. This civilization initially came into being in western Europe under the influence of the Islamic revolution. Its influence later spread all over the world. The negative aspect of this civilization is its emphasis on materialism to the exclusion of all else. Its positive aspect is its continuation of the effect of the Islamic revolution in emancipating human thought.

JOURNEY TOWARDS PROGRESS

There were four centres of civilization before the advent of Christ—Persia, China, India and Greece. After the advent of the Prophet of Islam, the Abbasid Caliph, Al-Mansoor, built Baghdad in 762. He invited religious scholars and intellectuals to come from far and near, and encouraged the rendering of books in various languages into Arabic. This work started under the patronage of the state. In 830 Al-Mamun established in Baghdad his famous Bayt al Hikmah, a combination library, academy and translation bureau, and an astronomical observatory. The work of translation continued with such speed and on such a vast scale that, within eighty years after the establishment of Baghdad, most of the books in Greek had already been rendered into Arabic.

During the Abbasid era, paper was being manufactured on a large scale, so there was no dearth of paper for writing books. There were more than 400,000 books in the library of Cordova (Spain) in the tenth century, whereas in Europe at that time, according to the Catholic Encyclopaedia, the library of Canterbury was at the top of the list of Christian libraries with 1800 books in the 13th century.

Al-Mamun's astronomers performed one of the most delicate geodetic operations—the measuring of the length of a terrestrial degree. The object was to determine the size of the earth and its circumference on the assumption that the earth was round. The measurement, carried out on the plain of Sinjar, north of the Euphrates, and near Palmyra, yielded 562 Arabic miles as the length of a degree of the meridian—a remarkably accurate result, exceeding the real length of the degree at that place by about 2877 feet. This would make the circumference of the earth 20,400 miles and its diameter 6500. Among those who took part in this operation were the sons of Musa ibn Shakir and al-Khwarizmi, whose tables, revised a century and a half later by the Spanish astronomer Maslamah al-Majriti and translated into Latin in 1126 by Adelard of Bath, became the bases for other works both in the East and the West. No less a feat was that of Al-Idrisi who, as early as the 12th century, made a map of the world in which he even showed the source of the River Nile, which was not discovered by Europe till the 19th century.

All these activities were going on in the world of Islam at a time when the whole of Europe believed that the earth was flat.

Ptolemy, the well-known Greek astronomer of the 2nd century, had presented the earth-centered theory of the solar system, in his famous book, *Almajest*. This concept dominated the minds of the people all over the world for about 1500 years, until, in the 16th century, Copernicus, Galileo and Kepler carried out researches which ultimately proved its falsity. But it was the Muslims, who first transferred to Europe the concept of the earth being round and the almost correct concept of the causes of the ebb and flow of the tides.

If a wrong concept about the revolution of the earth remained predominant for such a long period of time, it was due to the error of regarding something non-sacred as sacred. The Christians believed that the earth was a sacred sphere, being the birthplace of the son of God (Christ). Because of this belief, they found the notion that the earth was the centre around which the whole universe revolved exactly in accordance with their religious beliefs. It was this idea of the earth's sacredness which came in the way of the Christians making any further investigation. It was not until the naked reality finally forced itself upon them that they stopped adhering to this theory.

The *Encyclopaedia Britannica* (1984) says:

According to the old cosmology the Earth was the centre of the universe, man was the highest creature of this Earth, and his salvation was the central event in heaven and on Earth. The discovery that the Earth is only one planet among others that rotate around the sun, and that the sun is only an insignificant star among the innumerable galaxies of the cosmos, has shaken the old understanding of man. If the Earth, compared to the huge expanses of the universe, was only a speck of dust in the structure of the macrocosm, Newton and others began to explore the question of how man, the dust of dust, could continue to claim the holy privilege that he and his fame were the goal and culmination of God's actions.[13]

The Christians held Christ to be a part of the holy Trinity and developed the concept that the most important event of history ever to take place on earth was the crucifixion of God's son for the atonement of man's sins. In this way, the earth came to hold a sacred position in their set of beliefs. They offered the most stiff opposition to any such thinking as could undermine the central position of the earth. It was this belief that came in the way of free investigation of the solar system.

Holding the non-sacred to be sacred had thus locked the doors to all progress. Holding the moon sacred came in the way of nurturing the thought of man setting foot upon it. Holding the river sacred came in the way of man ever planning to produce electricity by conquering the river. Holding the cow sacred came in the way of man gauging the importance of its protein-rich meat and making it a part of his diet. All such research and investigation could start only when natural phenomena could be brought down from their pedestal of sanctity to a level on which man could look at them as normal, everyday things.

Prior to Islam, the stars were objects of veneration. But after the Islamic revolution, observatories were built and the stars were subjected to observational research on a large scale, something which had never previously been attempted. The minerals embedded in the earth's crust were likewise regarded as sacred. But Muslims, having developed the science of chemistry, subjected them for the first time to scientific examination. The entire earth for that matter was considered to be a deity. (It was even thought that the sky was a male deity and the earth a female deity!) The Muslims again were the first to measure it to find out its diameter and circumference. The sea, too, was an object of worship, but the Muslims became the greatest pioneers in using it as a vast highway. Storms and the wind were held to be mysterious forces and, as such, were objects of awe and reverence. The Muslims set them to turning their windmills.

Mysterious stories were associated with trees and thus the trees too had become worthy of veneration. The Muslims started investigating them, and succeeded in enriching Dioscorides' Herbal by 2000 species.

The rivers, too, were held to be sacred and therefore alive. Boys and girls were, therefore, sacrificed to these deities in order to please them. Muslims, however, used the same rivers for irrigation by making canals, thus ushering in a new age of agriculture.

In those days, Muslims were so ahead of other nations that when they were driven out of Spain, the astrolabes they left behind, by means of which they had studied heavenly bodies, were turned into the clock tower of a church, as the Christians did not understand their use.

It is a fact that in ancient times, polytheism and superstition held sway all over the world. And it is also true that it was this polytheism and superstition which were the major obstacles to all kinds of progress. The revolution based on monotheism which was brought about in the wake of Islam put an almost complete end to polytheism and superstition for the first time in history. Afterwards, as a natural result, human history took to the path of progress.

In ancient times, certain countries produced men with creative minds, who could think independently of their environment. But due to the unfavourable atmosphere and hostile environment of the times, their efforts could not be brought to fruition. The buds of their knowledge withered away before they could flower. However, when the Islamic revolution produced a favourable atmosphere, it unleashed a mighty flood of knowledge which had been kept pent up for thousands of years by the dam of superstition.

LEARNING AND ISLAM

Ptolemy II, who became the ruler of Egypt after Alexander the Great in the third century B.C., was a great patron of learning, and founded a library in Alexandria which contained about 500,000 books on different subjects. It is this collection which is known in history as the great library of Alexandria.

It has been alleged — wrongly, as it happens — that this library was burned down at the behest of the second caliph, 'Umar Farooq. It had , in fact, been destroyed much earlier, in the fourth century A.D., long before the advent of Islam. According to the *Encyclopaedia Britannica*, "The library survived the disintegration of Alexander's empire (1st century B.C.) and continued to exist under Roman rule until the third century A.D.."[14]

The truth is that one half of this library was burnt by Julius Caesar in 47 B.C. In the third century, Alexandria came under the domination of the Christians. With reference to the survival of existing institutions, the *Encyclopaedia Britannica* states that "the main museum and library were destroyed during the civil war of the third century A.D. and a subsidiary library was burned by Christians in A.D. 391."[15]

This same work, however, erroneously links the final destruction of the library with the Muslim period. In its article on censorship, it has this to say:

> There are many accounts of the burning, in several stages, of part or all of the library at Alexandria, from the siege of Julius Caesar in 47 B.C. to its destruction by Christians in A.D. 391 and by Muslims in 642. In the latter two instances, it was alleged that pagan literature presented a danger to the Old and New Testaments or the Qur'an.[16]

The above attribution of the destruction of the Alexandria library to Islam has no basis in fact. The first two extracts quoted above from the *Encyclopaedia Britannica* clearly refute this. Islam by its very nature, encourages the acquisition of knowledge. It has never been its aim to suppress or discourage it.

Philip Hitti states in his book, *History of the Arabs:*

> The story that by the caliph's order 'Amr for six long months

fed the numerous bath furnaces of the city with the volumes of
the Alexandrian library is one of those tales that make good fiction
but bad history. The great Ptolemaic library was burnt as early
as 48 B.C. by Julius Caesar. A later one, referred to as the
Daughter library, was destroyed about A.D. 389 as a result of an
edict by the Emperor Theodosius. At the time of the Arab
conquest, therefore, no library of importance existed in
Alexandria and no contemporary writer ever brought the charge
against ʿAmr or ʿUmar. ʿAbd al-Latif al-Baghdadi, who died as
late as A.H. 629 (1231), seems to have been the first to relate the
tale. Why he did it we do not know; however, his version was
copied and amplified by later authors.[17]

Islamic civilization is based on monotheism and, as such,
is quite distinct from other ancient civilizations. It gave man
freedom of thought—a freedom which was hitherto totally
lacking. Thanks to this freedom, learning had every
opportunity to flourish. In other older civilizations, learning
and learned people were commonly subjected to oppression.
It follows that the attempt to place Islamic civilization on
a parallel with other civilizations is a clear historical injustice.
This is not all that there is to the matter. The truth is that
it was actually Islam, not Europe, which heralded the age
of modern science. This is an undeniable historical event.
During the Islamic period, learning was actively encouraged,
and all fields of learning produced scholars and researchers
of repute. This has been generally acknowledged by
historians.

In an exhaustive book on the history of Islam, *The
Cambridge History of Islam*, produced by Professor P.M. Holt
and other orientalists, there is an article in volume 2-B,
entitled "Literary Impact of Islam in the Modern West,"

which shows the far-reaching influence exerted by Islam in the past on the learning and civilization of the western world. The chapter concludes with these words: ".... during the Middle Ages the trend was almost entirely from East to West (when Islam acted as the teacher of the West)."[18]

Another orientalist, the French Baron Carra de Vaux, underlines the achievements of the Arabs by stating that "the Arabs have really achieved great things in Science." "However" he goes on to say, "we must not expect to find among the Arabs the same powerful genius, the same gift of scientific imagination, the same enthusiasm, the same originality of thought that we have among the Greeks; their science is a continuation of Greek science which it preserves, cultivates, and on a number of points develops and perfects."[19]

Montgomery Watt, however, in his book entitled *The Majesty That Was Islam*, states that there is a tendency to belittle the work of the Arabs and to regard them as no more than transmitters of Greek ideas. He says that Arabs were much more than transmitters and that Arab science and philosophy contributed greatly to developments in Europe.[20]

This same author, however, makes another point which is more open to objection than the remark that Arabs were mere transmitters. He writes: "Science and philosophy in Arabic came into existence through the stimulus of translations from Greek."[21]

This statement that Greek science provided the stimulus to Arabs, so far as scientific ideas are concerned, is simply not true. It is not true to say that the Arabs read Greek translations which resulted in their beginning to think scientifically. The truth is that scientific thinking came to them through the Qur'an and the concept of monotheism. Later, they began studying translations of books from Greek and other languages, from which point they went on to the study of science and philosophy by carrying out their own research.

Historians have said that there is, of course, no denying the fact that the Arabs were the pupils of the Greeks in science and philosophy, but it is also true that once they had assimilated what was to be learnt from the Greeks, they went on to make important advances.[22]

Medicine was probably the first Greek science to attract the Arabs because of its obvious practical importance. Then they developed it to the extent of establishing medical colleges and hospitals, which did not exist in Greece. Not merely was it taught in the colleges of Iraq, but the teaching was accompanied by a flourishing medical service. The first hospital in Baghdad was founded about the year 800 on the initiative of the Caliph Harun al Rashid, and records have been preserved of the founding of four other hospitals there in the first quarter of the tenth century. A thirteenth century hospital in Cairo is said to have had accommodation for 8,000 persons. It had separate wards for male and female patients, as well as for different categories of ailment. The staff included physicians and surgeons, pharmacists, attendants of both sexes and administrative officers, and, besides store-rooms and a chapel, there were facilities for lecturing and a library.[23]

The Arabs thus made extraordinary advances in medicine through their research. The first important physician was Abu Bakr Muhammad ibn Zakariyya ar-Razi (d. 923), known in Europe as Rhazes. He wrote voluminously on many scientific and philosophic subjects, and over fifty of his works are extant. His greatest work, *Al-Havi*, was translated into Latin as the *Continens*, (the comprehensive book). It was the first encyclopaedia of all medical science up to that time, and had to be completed by his disciples after his death. For each disease he gave the views of Greek, Syrian, Indian, Persian and Arabic authors, and then added notes on his clinical observations and expressed a final opinion.

The greatest writer on medicine was Ibn Sina or Avicenna. He was also one of the two greatest Arabic philosophers. His eminence in medicine was due to his ability to combine extensive theoretical knowledge and systematic thought with acute clinical observation. His vast *Canon of Medicine (Al-Qanun fi't-Tib)* was translated into Latin in the twelfth century and was used much more than the works of Galen and Hippocrates. It dominated the teaching of medicine in Europe until at least the end of the sixteenth century. There were sixteen printed editions of it in the fifteenth century, one being in Hebrew, twenty editions in the sixteenth century and several more in the seventeenth. Roughly contemporary with Avicenna was the chief Arabic writer on surgery and surgical instruments, Abul Qasim az-Zohrawi (d. after 1009), usually known in Latin as Abulcasis.

While Arabic medicine thus reached its highest point in the early eleventh century, it continued to hold sway for many more centuries. The gift of careful observation did not disappear and certain fourteenth century Arab doctors in Spain wrote knowledgeably, about the plague as they had experienced it in Granada and Almeria.[24]

Abdullah ibn Baytar (d. 1248) was the best known botanist and pharmacist of Spain, in fact, of the Muslim world. He travelled as a herbalist in Spain and throughout North Africa, and later entered the service of the Ayyubid al-Malik al- Kamil in Cairo as chief herbalist. From Egypt he made extensive trips throughout Syria and Asia Minor. One of his two celebrated works, *Al-Mughni fi al Adwiyah al-Mufradah,* is on materia medica. The other, *Al-Jami' fi al-Adwiya al-Mufradah,* is a collection of "simple remedies from the animal, vegetable and mineral worlds embodying Greek and Arabic data supplemented by the author's own experiments and researches." It stands out as the foremost medieval treatise of its kind. Some 1400 items are considered, of which 300, including about 200 plants, were novelties. The number of authors quoted is about one hundred and fifty, of whom twenty were Greek. Parts of the Latin version of Ibn al Baytar's *Simplicia* were printed as late as 1758 at Cremona.[25]

After materia medica, astronomy and mathematics, the Arabs made their greatest scientific contribution in chemistry. This brought chemistry out of the sphere of alchemy and gave it the status of a regular science based on observation. In the study of chemistry and other physical sciences the Arabs introduced the objective experiment, a decided improvement over the hazy speculations of the Greeks. It was through them that the world was first introduced to the scientific method.

After al-Razi, Jabir ibn Hayyan (721-815) is ranked greatest in the field of medieval chemical science. He more clearly recognized and stated the importance of experimentation than any other early alchemist, and made noteworthy advances in both the theory and practice of chemistry.[26]

Jabir's books were held as the final authority on chemistry in Europe uptill the fifteenth century. The initial ladder to the modern western chemistry of the eighteenth century was produced by Jabir. It is believed that Jabir wrote two thousand books on different sciences. So many scholarly books had never been written before the Muslim epoch by any single writer.

These are only some scattered and incomplete references. They are, however, enough to show that Islam, far from being hostile to learning, is keenly supportive of it. In ancient times, the anti-learning tradition was laid down by those religions which were based on polytheism and superstition. Islam ended polytheism and superstition and established religion on the basis of pure monotheism. There is, therefore, no question of Islam becoming the enemy of knowledge and research.

The progress of learning is anathema to polytheism. Polytheistic religions, therefore, attempt to block its path. Monotheism, on the contrary, takes a very different stand, for the progress of learning verifies monotheism, thus establishing it all the more soundly. That is why monotheistic religion gives it every encouragement.

ISLAM: THE LIBERATOR OF THE MIND

In ancient times, an intellectual climate dominated by polytheism tended to encourage the spread of superstition throughout the world. Such an atmosphere was necessarily unfavourable to the emergence of scientific ideas; that is why there was no country during that period in which learning and science could progress. It was only when the Islamic revolution put an end to this age-old harnessing of the intellect to polytheism that attitudes began, effectively, to change.

ANCIENT GREECE

In ancient Greece, where every object had a god or goddess associated with it, the greatest influence on the human mind was that of mythology—a collection of innumerable legends about lofty, immortal beings and superhuman heroes. Although an aura of mysticism surrounded their origins and deeds, the early Greeks regarded the mythological creatures as historical realities of whom they remained in great awe. (Whole volumes have been written on this very vast subject, including an encyclopaedia.)

Greek mythology formed the staple of most Greek poetry and drama. It also influenced the thinking of philosophers and historians to a marked degree. Medieval poets and nearly all the English poets from Shakespeare to

Robert Bridges turned to it for inspiration. But stimulating as it was to the arts and literature, it failed to provide the kind of ambience in which men of science, in the modern sense of the word, could flourish.

The Greeks may have had the most illustrious civilization of ancient times, but they did nothing to set in motion the processes of scientific thinking, which came much later to Europe. If scientific thought reached Europe, it was entirely due to the stimulus given to it by the Muslims, for, up to that point, the concept of polytheism had acted as a deterrent to progress. The concept of monotheism, on the contrary, ushered in a whole new era of intellectual liberty.

ROMAN CIVILIZATION

The *Encyclopaedia Britannica* writes:

> Towards the close of the pre-Christian period, the Roman Empire achieved dominance over the entire Mediterranean world. Rome presents a paradox to historians of science. This civilization, so sophisticated and apparently modern in its politics and personalities, very strong in the learned disciplines of the law, very progressive in the state technologies of warfare and public hygiene, with direct access to the corpus of Greek science, nevertheless failed to produce a single scientist.[27]

The article goes on to say that historians, attempting to explain the Romans' utter failure in science, suggest that "perhaps the social structure of Rome, combined with its long adherence to gross forms of magic, left no place for an appreciation of that peculiar commitment to the hard and hazardous road to knowledge and wisdom that lies through disciplined enquiry into isolated aspects of the natural world. Indeed, when one considers how few have been the cultures in which science has flourished, one may reverse the question and consider Rome as the normal, and classical Greece as the surprising phenomenon to be explained."[28]

The historians have failed to produce any convincing answer to this question. But the answer becomes obvious when we take into account the fact that the Romans were polytheists. It was actually polytheism and idol worship which stood in the way of their carrying out research and investigation in the field of science. The concept of the sanctity of all natural objects prevented them from making a conquest of them.

THE DAWN OF THE SCIENTIFIC AGE

The *Encyclopaedia Britannica* states under the heading of "History of Science" that the present way of comprehending the natural world is a very recent development. It was possible for great civilizations of the past to achieve highly developed technologies and religious and legal systems in the complete absence of a conception of science as it is now understood. Such were the civilizations of ancient Egypt, Mesopotamia, India and the western hemisphere. Even the Hebrews, people whose religion forms a large part of the basis of European civilization, were indifferent to science. Although some two and a half millennia ago the Greeks created a system of thought that was similar to the scientific, in succeeding centuries there was little progress beyond their achievement and little comprehension of it. The great power of science and its pervasive influence on all aspects of life are thus very recent developments.

The dawn of European science has traditionally been located among the philosophers of the Greek city states on the coast and islands of the eastern Mediterranean, in the later sixth and fifth centuries B.C. Their work is known only through fragmentary references, and brief quotations made by authors who came later, perhaps by hundreds of years.[29]

These brief references are actually very misleading. For example, the saying of the earliest known philosopher, Thales, "All is water," would appear to be a scientific sentence. But when taken as a whole—"All is water, and the world is full of gods,"[30] it assumes a superstitious character. (Thales was a philosopher who lived in the sixth century B.C. None of his writings or contemporary source materials survive. His name is included in the canon of the legendary seven wise men.)

The truth is that for both Greeks and Romans, there was only one barrier obstructing the path of science, and that was their polytheistic thinking. This indeed was what had robbed them of the realistic bent of mind which is so essential to scientific investigation. There was, therefore, no question of their ever making any progress in this field.

JOURNEY TOWARDS PROGRESS

Many great scientific minds were born in ancient times in the European country of Greece, one of them being Archimedes, who made great strides in hydrostatics, even inventing a simple machine—the water screw. But it is strange that these Greek scientific minds shone only temporarily, like meteors, and then disappeared. They failed to usher Europe, or even Greece itself, into the age of science and industry. A very long intellectual gap is found between the learning of the ancient Greeks and that of modern scientific Europe. While Archimedes had invented the water screw as early as 260 B.C., the first machine press was not invented until 1450, by Germany's J. Gutenberg. The interval between the two is more than one thousand five hundred years.

What was the reason for this gap? Why did ancient Greek science find no continuation either in Greece or elsewhere in Europe? The answer is that before the Islamic revolution, the atmosphere was totally opposed to scientific research being freely carried out. It was not until the revolution brought about by Islam, on the basis of monotheism, that all obstacles could be removed from the path of scientific progress. This was the first time in history that there had been such a liberation of the intellect.

Scientific progress, to be effective, must be a continuous process. The work of the Greek scholars, however, due to the unpropitious circumstances of the times, could not advance in this way. It shone forth momentarily, then disappeared from the scene. Then in the seventh century Hijrah, when the Islamic revolution had put an end to the age of superstition, many favourable opportunities presented themselves to scientific research, which was subsequently carried on in an unbroken line right up to modern times.

Due to the earlier unfavourable atmosphere, the Greek scholars confined their work largely to the field of theory. They did not carry out practical experiments. For instance, Aristotle wrote treatises on physics, but, throughout his entire life, he did not carry out a single experiment. While the Greek scholars contributed greatly to the field of logic, they made no worthwhile contribution in the field of empirical science. The real beginning of science was made when the spirit of free enquiry was created in man. In ancient times, this spirit manifested itself sporadically on the part of individuals, but due to the hostile environment, this could not develop on a large scale.

An environment truly conducive to free enquiry emerged only after the monotheistic revolution of Islam. The whole atmosphere was instantly changed by it, paving the way for the work of investigation to go on unhampered. This scientific way of thinking had its beginnings in Mecca. Then it spread to Medina and Damascus, from where it went on to make Baghdad a great centre of innovative thought. From Baghdad, it found its way to Spain, Sicily and Italy, finally spreading all over Europe. It went on spreading, ultimately changing the universal mind.

This evolutionary journey of learning had not been possible before the Islamic revolution. Prior to this, scientific thinking had taken place only at the individual level, or in isolated places and, due to the adversarial atmosphere, it failed to flourish. Islam, for the first time, gave to the world an atmosphere which actively fostered scientific progress.

2
Holding Sacred that which is not Sacred

The noted anthropologist, Nathan Soderblom, observed in a work completed in 1913 that the notion of holiness formed the central concept of religion. Since then the history of religions has been studied on a vast scale, a large number of scholarly books having been written on the subject in German, French, English and other languages. With very few exceptions, scholars of religion are in agreement that holiness is the basic tenet of religion, that is, the attribution of such mystical qualities or powers to certain persons or things as are not ever found in ordinary creatures or objects. These mystical attributes cannot be explained by general, rational principles or concepts.[31]

This concept of holiness is not an imaginary thing; it is deeply ingrained in the nature of man. The feeling generated by it is properly employed when it is concentrated exclusively on God. But it frequently happens that this urge within man is diverted to something which, in actual fact, is not holy. The actual feeling of reverence for holiness, which should have been directed towards the Creator, finds its way instead towards some creature.

The reason for this is God's invisibility. Unable to see his Maker, man gives his attention to whatever else strikes him as most prominent in his immediate surroundings; he then begins to invest it with sanctity and to worship it as if it were genuinely holy. It is this psychology which produced in ancient times what is called polytheism in religious terminology, and nature worship in academic parlance. This basic urge to worship impelled man from within to revere something which was holy. Consequently, he started worshipping anything which made a great visual impact upon him, e.g. stars, rain, animals, plants, water and fire. The concept of an exalted God existed as the prophets had taught man. But this concept came to be distorted to mean that God "was the Lord in heaven who had withdrawn from the immediate details of governing the world. This kind of high God, a hidden, or idle God, had delegated all work on earth to these 'nature spirits,' which were the forces, or personifications of the forces of nature."[32]

Scholars of religion agree in general that the concept of holiness is the cohesive force in all religions. That is, for a religion to hold together, some unique or extraordinary person or thing must be designated as sacred and stand at the apex of the sum of its beliefs. This cannot be explained in terms of general, rational principles.

The commonest human reactions to objects of sanctity are fear and fascination. Only the sacred can fulfill man's deepest needs and aspirations. Thus, the reverence that man shows for whatever is held sacred is composed both of trust and of terror. There is also the view that the acceptance of something as sacrosanct signals the boundaries of human effort, where man's inherent limitations prevent him from seeking any further.

The objects of man's reverence are disparate in nature, e.g stones, animals, the sea, the sun, the moon, kings and other religious personalities. Whatever is held sacred is worshipped, and sacrifices, made to it. Rituals are observed in order to please it, escape its punishments and elicit its favours.

"Sacredness is manifested," observes the *Encyclopaedia Britannica*, in "sacred officials, such as priests and kings; in specially designated sacred places such as temples and images, and in natural objects, such as rivers, the sun, mountains, or trees. The priest is a special agent in the religious cult, his ritual actions represent the divine action. Similarly, the king or emperor is a special mediator between heaven and earth and has been called by such names as the 'son of heaven,' or an 'arm of god. "[33]

The following important anthropologists are listed by the *Encyclopaedia Britannica* as holding sacredness to be the basis of religion: Nathan Soderblom, Rudolf Otto, Emile Durkheim, Max Scheler, Gerardus Van der Leeuw, W. Brede Kristemsen, Friedrich Heiler, Gustov Mensching, Roger Caillois, Mircea Eliade.[34]

Modern scholars of religion are right in saying that the basic idea behind religion is the concept of holiness, which they claim is a natural feeling. However, when some other object besides one God is considered holy, this is the wrong application of a real, natural feeling. And this is the root cause of all kinds of evils. When man holds the non-holy as holy, he closes all manner of doors to progress.

There are two aspects of holding the non-holy as holy. One is to consider all of nature as being sacred, while the other is to revere certain individuals as being sacrosanct. Both kinds of evils have been found all over the world since ancient times. This has been the greatest reason for man's thinking having remained unscientific.

The notion of holiness is deeply rooted in human psychology. To define in a phrase such a psychology is extremely difficult, for the words used to express profound psychological states are more often symbolic than realistic. I would simply agree in principle that the concept of holiness is the focal point of religion. The existence of holiness, is, nevertheless, real and not imaginary, as modern scholars of religion would have us believe.

The truth is that the urge to worship is a natural instinct which every man is born with. Man, because of this deep inner urge, wants actively to bow before something which he regards as sacred. There are two forms in which this feeling finds expression: one is monotheism, the other polytheism.

When man holds one God sacred and worships him as his Deity, he directs his feelings to the proper place. It is, in reality, God who possesses the attribute of sacredness. Holding the one and only God sacred is, therefore, to acknowledge a great truth.

But the mistake man makes is to worship and revere whatever object he finds outstanding in this world, or whatever he finds different from himself, imagining it to be sacred. This is the wrong use of the right feeling. This is giving to a non-god what is due to the one and only God. In religious terminology this is known as polytheism or, in common parlance, superstition.

It was this error of sanctifying mere things instead of God Himself which prevented the emergence of science for thousands of years in the past. When we believe in one God, no scientific or intellectual problem arises in doing so, for God is beyond our physical reach and our sphere of functioning. He is beyond the heavens, through which man cannot pass.

The material objects which are considered holy, fall, on the other hand, within the sphere of human action. And whenever these things have been surrounded with an aura of holy mystery, they have assumed too exalted a status to be subjected to scientific investigation. It is precisely in making an intellectual conquest of these things that science has had its beginnings.

All things other than God are mere creatures. These are generally known as natural phenomena. It is these phenomena which provide the groundwork for science. To study them and to conquer and control them is what is meant by scientific procedure.

From ancient times the phenomena of nature had universally been considered sacred; as such, far from being objects of conquest, they all became objects of worship. It was this intellectual distortion which prevented scientific action for thousands of years in the past. The door to progress opened only when the revolution of monotheism changed human thinking and brought nature down from its pedestal of holiness.

AN EXAMPLE

Polytheism, a world-wide phenomenon in ancient times, is now mainly confined to the Indian sub-continent, where, with its emphasis on vegetarianism, it is still extant in a powerful, living form. However, it has come to be viewed as an obstacle to the application of the results of modern, academic research.

Just how large an obstacle became clear when in 1967, the eminent scientist, Dr M.S. Swaminathan, the then Director of the Indian Agricultural Institute, New Delhi, made his views on nutrition known in an interview with an English daily. Speaking to a representative of UNI, Dr Swaminathan said, "India may have to face the danger of large scale intellectual dwarfing in two decades if the problem of malnutrition and 'protein hunger' is not tackled soon." He explained that while the concept of balanced nutrition was not new, its significance to brain development was a recent biological discovery.

"It is now clear that the human brain reaches 80% to 90% of its full weight by the age of four, and if children do not get adequate protein during this 'critical period,' the brain does not develop properly," Dr Swaminathan stated and went on to say that comparative studies on the intelligence of different ethnic groups would in the future have to be viewed from this standpoint too. If the problems of malnutrition and protein hunger were not taken in hand immediately, "We may have to witness during the next two decades a growing acuteness of intellectual power in the developed nations, but a process of intellectual dwarfing in our own country. Every day's delay in fighting protein hunger in the youth could lead to the creation of more than 10 million 'intellectual dwarfs.'" He added: "Much damage must have already occurred in recent years." Asked for a solution to the problem, Dr Swaminathan said, "The message of protein-consciousness should be carried to the masses by government action and the mobilisation of public opinion."

He explained that pulses constituted the most important protein source in a vegetarian diet, whereas animal products like milk had proteins of a better quality. Protein needs would have to be assessed both in terms of quantity and quality. Among the components of protein, about 80 amino acids were necessary for normal growth. He said that a deficiency of some of the acids like lycine and methionine were common in a vegetarian diet, while the excess of leucine in Jowar had been the cause of diseases in certain areas where this cereal was the staple food. Though a larger consumption of animal products was desirable, their production was costly since much energy was wasted in converting plant products into animal food.[35]

After the publication of this interview, the *Indian*

Express brought out an editorial titled, 'Protein Hunger,' which said:

> ...when the union government decided to go in for a comprehensive policy of price support for foodgrains, it could hardly have been suspected that there could be 'protein hunger' in view of the plentiful supply of cereals.

> As the Director of the Indian Agricultural Research Institute, Dr M.S. Swaminathan, has pointed out, an over-dependence on cereals could lead to a situation in which even well-fed people are under-nourished. Besides the physical handicaps from which those who are starved of proteins may suffer, the mental side-effect of this, according to Dr Swaminathan, would be that the mental capacity of children would not develop properly.

> Viewed in this light, a re-examination of the present agricultural policy is necessary. But the limitations within which the Government must act are also many. First of all, it is very expensive to transform farm produce into animal protein. Besides, even though the Government has conducted a campaign for balanced diets and higher consumption of meat, eggs and fish, the people have been slow to change their eating habits.[36]

People reacted strongly to Dr Swaminathan's statement. Some extremists even demanded his resignation, saying that he was not fit for the presidentship of a national institute. In view of such an adverse reaction, Swaminathan had no choice but to fall silent. The matter became a closed topic.

The reason for this strong, public reaction was that according to the traditional religion of India, the taking of a life is the worst possible sin. Since living things must be killed to produce non-vegetarian food, vegetarianism has become the order of the day. The cow, in particular, must never be slaughtered because, in this religious context, it is a sacred animal. The Rigveda has called the cow a goddess.[37]

This makes it clear how certain aspects of polytheistic faiths have become an obstacle to human progress.

India is rich in resources and opportunities. Despite this abundance, it has yet to become a developed country. Chiefly to blame for this are the polytheistic constraints which hinder the march of progress. Not until the country is set free of all such unrealistic limitations will India truly set its feet on the path of progress.

THE EMERGENCE OF SCIENCE

In the history of Europe the period from the sixth to the tenth century A.D. is known as the Dark Ages. This is a period when Europe was far from being civilized. "For Europe it was a period of intellectual darkness and barbarity."[38]

The term 'Dark Ages' was applicable, however, only to Europe; when Europe was enveloped in the murk of the Dark Ages, the light of civilization shone brightly throughout the world of Islam. As Bertrand Russell puts it in his *History of Western Philosophy*, "From India to Spain, the brilliant civilization of Islam flourished."[39]

This Islamic civilization, which entered Europe via Sicily and Spain, exerted a strong influence there, so much so that students from western Europe started coming to receive their education in the Islamic universities of Spain. Many from the Muslim world likewise went to Europe. When

Europeans realised that the Muslims had gone far ahead of them in education, they began to render books written by Muslim scholars into Latin. The *Encyclopaedia Britannica* says: "Most of the classical literature that spurred the European Renaissance was obtained from translations of Arabic manuscripts in Muslim libraries."[40]

In modern times, a large number of scholars, for instance, Gustav Liban, Robert Briffault, J.M. Robert, Montgomery Watt, and so on, have clearly acknowledged that it was the investigations and discoveries of the Arabs that paved the way for modern science in Europe. It would be correct to say that this is a universally known fact. The only point on which we must differ is that the event recorded as 'Muslim history' should come under the heading of 'Islamic history.' An event thus attributed to a people should have been attributed rather to God.

SOME EXAMPLES

In ancient times certain things were considered holy according to the polytheistic set of beliefs then prevalent. This mentality had closed the door to independent thinking on the subject of natural phenomena. Then came the revolution brought about by monotheism. For the first time in human history, this produced the right atmosphere for freedom of enquiry. All things then began to be studied without any hesitation. The monotheistic revolution thus founded the very first original basis for scientific thinking along systematic lines. Scientific research had, of course, been carried out prior to this, but, due to the unfavourable atmosphere, it had not been welcomed with approval or recognition. Without this, no further advances could be made in this sphere.

Galileo (d. 1442) is generally considered to be the inventor of the telescope. But the truth is that, long before his time, Abu Ishaq ibn Jundub (d. 767) had already made observations of the heavens. He had devised certain rules for observing distant objects and, in accordance with those rules, he had invented a telescopic instrument. It was this initial telescope which was further developed by Galileo, and which was the actual forerunner of the now highly perfected electric telescope of modern times.

The basis of modern science is observation. But, in ancient times, several kinds of superstitious beliefs barred the way to such activity. Jabir ibn Hayyan (d. 817), however, understanding the importance of observation, used findings based thereon in his scientific studies, the written accounts of which were transmitted to Europe in translations. Thinking went on developing along these lines until it formed the basis for experimental science as it is known today.

The first person in history to advance the theory of inertia in material bodies was Ali Hasan ibn al-Haysam (d. 1021). This discovery reached Europe, where scholars subjected it to further scrutiny. It was formulated much later, as Newton's law of motion, namely, that every body continues in its state of rest or uniform motion in a straight line, except in so far as it is compelled by external forces to change that state. Then again it was ibn Haysam who originally discovered that the path taken by a ray of light or other wave motion in traversing the distance between any two points is such that the time taken is a minimum. This discovery later became known as Fermat's principle of least time.

THE AGE OF THE EARTH

Scientists have not been able to agree on the date of man's emergence on earth. However, they have discovered some human skeleton which they believe to date back to ten thousand years before Christ. The scientists do not, therefore, accept the assertions on this subject made by the Bible. According to the dates for the appearance of the human race given in the book of Genesis, Adam came to the world thirty seven hundred years before Christ. The Jewish calendar, which follows the data contained in the Old Testament, places the dates very precisely. The second half of the Christian year 1975 corresponds to the beginning of the 5,736th year of the creation of the world. According to modern science, this is wholly unacceptable.

The Christians, as it would appear from biblical narratives, had condensed the life-span of the earth to within a few thousand years. The error of this calculation, from the scientific point of view, came to light in the eighteenth century when James Hutton, a great geologist, carried out his investigations. He devoted his whole life to studying the construction of the earth and its rocks, which showed that the earth in its present form has evolved over millions of years.

ISLAM: CREATOR OF THE MODERN AGE

Charles Lyell's observations subsequently confirmed Hutton's theory. The first volume of his renowned book, *Principles of Geology*, was first published in 1830. This book was to a great extent responsible for the disappearance of the biblical time-scale from all serious discussion. "Indeed, Lyell's books were largely responsible for convincing the world at large that the Bible could be wrong, at any rate in some respects—a hitherto unthinkable thought."[41]

Concepts of the kind enshrined in the Bible acted as barriers to the scientific progress of Europe. Anyone who dared to present any theory other than those approved of by the Church risked being severely chastised on the grounds that his theory was sacrilegious. But, in Islam, such unreal concepts had never gained currency. That is why no religious opposition presented itself when scientific research began in Islamic Spain.

GREEK SCIENCES

The modern age of progress began in Europe between the fourteenth and sixteenth centuries. This age is generally referred to as the Renaissance, which means revival, or rebirth. The Europeans associate this age of renaissance with Greece, a European country. They present the modern age of Europe as being, in fact, a revival of the ideas of Greek antiquity. But the truth is that Europe went through a period of awakening, rather than of rebirth or revival. And this was the first time in the history of Europe that this had happened. Now scholars have accepted that the Renaissance of the West is a direct gift from the Arabs. Briffault writes:

> The debt of our science to that of the Arabs does not consist in startling discoveries of revolutionary theories. Science owes a great deal more to Arab culture. It owes its existence.[42]

He goes on to say:

> It is highly probable that but for the Arabs, modern industrial civilization would never have arisen at all.[43]

The *Encyclopaedia Britannica* (1984) says that libraries formed important features of Islamic society. There were a number of institutions which possessed more than one lakh books. Most of the classical literature that spurred the European Renaissance was obtained from translations of Arabic manuscripts in Muslim libraries.[44]

To some, the achievement of the Arabs is at best their transmission of the Greek sciences to Europe through translations. Professor Hitti puts it in these words:

> This stream (of Greek culture) was redirected into Europe by the Arabs in Spain and Sicily, whence it helped create the Renaissance of Europe.[45]

Such an assertion is not, however, correct, for what the Arabs had received from Greek philosophers was not experimental knowledge but theoretical argument. In other words, what they received from the Greeks was not science but philosophy. Science, as we now understand it had never existed in Greece. Science, or knowledge based on experimentation, is the invention of the Muslims. It was the Muslims who first attained to knowledge through observation, and then communicated it to other nations, particularly those situated in Europe.

Bertrand Russell has rightly said:

> Science, ever since the time of the Arabs, has had two functions: (1) to enable us to know things and (2) to enable us to do things. The Greeks, with the exception of Archimedes, were only interested in the first of these ... interest in the practical uses of science came first through superstition and magic.[46]

He goes on to say:

> To modern educated people, it seems obvious that matters of fact are to be ascertained by observation, not by consulting ancient authorities. But this is an entirely modern conception, which hardly existed before the seventeenth century. Aristotle maintained that women have fewer teeth than men; although he was twice married, it never occurred to him to verify this statement by examining his wives' mouths.[47]

Citing further examples of this nature, Russell observes that Aristotle made many assertions about things without ever observing them, and that his adherents continued to repeat them without putting them to the test of observation.

It is essential for scientists to observe and experiment on things in depth to have a correct knowledge of their nature. But an atmosphere conducive to such procedures did not exist among the Greeks or in other ancient nations. Because objects other than God had sacredness attributed to them, they developed an aura of mystery and became sacrosanct in the eyes of the peoples. This resulted in magic, superstition and the worship of non-gods becoming widely prevalent.

These grave misconceptions stood in the way of scientific enquiry into the nature of things. When people believe that events take place by magic, or that natural phenomena have divine properties of a mystical nature, no thinking can develop which will lead to research on the nature of these things. In such an atmosphere, it is but natural that such a mentality will develop as will grovel to magic and superstition.

The Arabs of ancient times had similarly been held in thrall by superstition. For them too, as in other nations, it had become a mental block. But when an intellectual revolution was brought about amongst them by Islam, this mental block very soon evaporated. Now they began to look at things as they were, whereas prior to this revolution they had viewed the same objects as sacred and mysterious. It is this intellectual revolution which produced among Arabs scientific thinking for the first time in human history. By developing this line of thought, they became the giver people; they gave to the whole world what in modern times, is called science.

PHYSICAL SCIENCES

Arnold Toynbee, the renowned twentieth century English historian, tells us that science is another name for the exploitation of nature. He then raises the question as to why man took so long to control and exploit it when it had existed in our world for millions of years. He himself gives us the answer:

> For ancient man nature was not just a treasure trove of 'natural resources,' but a goddess, 'Mother Earth.' And the vegetation that

sprang from the earth, the animals that roamed the earth's surface, and the minerals hiding in the earth's bowels, all partook of nature's divinity, so did all natural phenomena—springs and rivers and the sea; mountains; earthquakes and lightning and thunder. Such was the original religion of all mankind.[48]

When nature is regarded as an object of worship, it cannot, at the same time, be looked at as an object of exploitation, investigation and conquest. Referring to the historical fact mentioned above, Toynbee acknowledges that the age in which nature was sacrosanct was brought to an end only with the advent of monotheism. The concept of monotheism brought nature down from being a deity set upon a high pedestal to being just another part of God's Creation. Now, instead of the phenomena of nature being held as objects of worship, they came to be held as objects of subjugation and conquest.

This concept of monotheism had been propounded by all the prophets in the past. However, it remained at the level of pronouncement on an individual level; it could not reach the stage of general revolution. The movement based on monotheism finally reached the stage of revolution only through the struggle of the Prophet and his companions. After this, the tendency to regard nature as holy decreased to the point where it no longer existed as such; this was a necessary outcome of such a revolution. Now man started looking at nature with a view to exploring and exploiting it. This process developed in a positive way over the centuries, sometimes slowing, sometimes accelerating, but finally ushering in our modern scientific age.

The *Encyclopaedia Britannica* states in its article, 'History of Physical Sciences,' that Greek science fell into jeopardy after the second century A.D., because the Romans were not interested in it."Social pressures, political persecution and the anti-intellectual bias of the church Fathers drove the few remaining Greek scientists and philosophers to the East. There they ultimately found a welcome when the rise of Islam in the seventh century stimulated interest in scientific and philosophic subjects. Most of the important Greek scientific texts were preserved in Arabic translations. Although the Arabs did not alter the foundations of Greek science, they made several important contributions within its general framework, and when the interest in Greek learning revived in western Europe during the twenfthand thirteenth centuries, scholars turned to Islamic Spain for the scientific texts. A spate of translations (from Arabic into Latin) resulted in the revival of science in the west ... scientists of the Middle Ages reached high levels of sophistication and prepared the ground for the scientific revolution of the sixteenth and seventeenth centuries."[49]

Moseoleban asserts in his book, *Arab Civilization*, that Arab sciences reached Europe not through the crusades, but by way of Andalusia, Sicily and Italy. In 1130, an institute for translation was established under the patronage of Remond of Taletala, through which famous books were rendered into Latin from Arabic, and through these translations a whole new world was opened up to Europe. This work of translation continued right up to the fourteenth century. Not only the works of Ar Razi, Avicena and Averroes, but also those of Galen, Hippocrates, Plato, Aristotle, Eucleides, Ptolemy, etc. were translated from Arabic into Latin. Dr. Guilkirk, in his book on the history of this period, mentions more than three hundred books translated from Arabic into Latin.

Other western scholars have even more openly acknowledged this as a historical fact. Robert Briffault, for example, has written that the Greeks produced system, generalized it, formulated it, but that it was alien to their temperament to go into the labour of observation and experimental research. George Sarton, the famous chronicler of scientific advances, writes that the most fundamental and most distinctive success lay in fostering the latter activities and that what ultimately came to be called science was the result of a new method of experiment, observation and calculation originally brought into being by the Muslims.

This spirit of enquiry prevailed until the twelfth century, and was transmitted to Europe through the Arabs. Modern science is, indeed, the greatest legacy of the Islamic civilization.

THE GIFT OF ISLAM

The two most important contributions of Islam in this connection were, firstly, to remove any mental block which could be an obstacle to progress, and secondly, to launch the new age of progress on a practical basis.

Removing the mental block meant displacing things from their pedestals of holiness. This task—undoubtedly the most difficult—was successfully performed during the period of the Prophet and the pious Caliphs who succeeded him.

Although a practical beginning had been made in the first phase of Islam, its systematic development took place during the Abbasid era with the establishment of the Bayt-al-Hikmah in 832. This work gained great momentum during the Arab rule in Spain and Sicily. Finally, it reached Europe, where it gave the first impetus to the industrial revolution.

It is generally accepted that modern progress and its ramifications are related to industrial revolution. In fact, it could be said that all progress has come in its wake. Industrial revolution itself is another name for the exploitation of the hidden resources of the earth. For example, man mined coal and then converted it into energy. He harnessed the power of flowing water and converted that into electricity. He extracted minerals from beneath the earth's surface and transformed them into machines. And this is how the industrial revolution came into existence.

Now, why was it, that when all these resources had been available on the earth since time immemorial, man had not been able to utilize them in order to found a developed civilization prior to the advent of Islam? There is only one answer: polytheism had placed an insurmountable barrier in his path.

What is polytheism? It is the worship of the phenomena of nature. Before the time of the Prophet of Islam, in every period recorded in history, man had worshipped natural phenomena, holding them to be imbued with divinity. All ancient civilizations— Greek, Egyptian, Roman and Persian—all were polytheistic in their persuasions. All the outstanding things of this world—earth, rivers, mountains, sun, moon or stars—all were objects of worship for man. Only Islam was able to displace them from the pedestal of worship. Only then could that new intellectual departure be made which is now known as the scientific revolution.

3
Muslim Contribution to Science

An atmosphere of free investigation is essential to the progress of science. In former times, however, such an atmosphere was extremely rare, thanks to various kinds of man-made beliefs. There were many cases in those days of an intelligent, scholarly person discovering a certain truth while pondering over his subject, only to find people turning against him and his discovery because they found it clashing with their superstitious beliefs. That was why new, innovative thinking could not make any progress.

One of the most notorious examples of the suppression of new ideas in antiquity was the condemnation of the renowned Greek philosopher, Socrates, to death, by drinking hemlock in 399 B.C. He was accused of ignoring the gods worshipped by the Athenians, of making new inventions in religion and of corrupting the youth of Athens.

Another such example—as late as the seventeenth century—was that of Galileo (1564-1642), the Italian astronomer who offended the Church simply by endorsing the Copernican view of the planets moving round the sun. He was sentenced by a religious court and thrown into prison. When he saw that death awaited him, he was forced to recant before the Inquisition. Kneeling, with both his hands on the Bible, he solemnly withdrew his 'far-fetched' theory of the movement of the planets around the sun. He not only rejected this theory, but said that he considered it 'abominable.'

This was not just an isolated incident, but rather a symptom of the intellectual malaise created by the Christian scholars of those times. The search for new truths and the discovery of nature's secrets remained forbidden pastures to them for centuries. Such activities were reviled as black magic and a part of satanic teachings. In such circumstances, it was impossible for the processes of research and investigation to be carried on with any success. In the Middle Ages, it was solely due to the Muslims that such work could be given any impetus, thanks to the Qur'an having removed the kind of mental blocks that had stood in the way of people of other faiths, such as Galileo.

An appropriate attitude to scientific matters began to be encouraged for the first time after the Islamic revolution. This process then went on unhampered, ultimately leading to the age of modern discoveries.

THE SOLAR SYSTEM

The astronomer who is said to have studied the solar system and presented the heliocentric theory for the first time was a Greek, known by the name of Aristarchus of Samos. He died in 270 B.C. However, this theory of the sun being at the centre, and of the earth revolving around it, never gained popularity in those early times.

Then came the age of Ptolemy, who lived in the second century A.D. Ptolemy's astronomical system represented the earth as the fixed centre of the universe, with the sun and the moon, and other stars and planets revolving around it.

This geocentric theory of the universe appeared to be in conformity with the beliefs the Christians had developed after Jesus Christ. These beliefs were given the final seal of approval at the famous Church Council held at Nicaea, a city in Asia Minor, in A.D. 325. After the acceptance of Christianity by Constantine the Great (280-337), the faith spread all over Roman territory. Now vested with tremendous power, the Christians patronized, in particular, the theory of Ptolemy. The curtain of darkness fell over the heliocentric theory of Aristarchus.

Of geocentricity the *Encyclopaedia Britannica* (1984) says: "There was no further scope for cosmology in the model, which continued to be taught and used almost everywhere until the 17th century."[50]

It was not until 1495 that Copernicus arrived at the conclusion that the earth was not the centre of the universe. After a long period of research devoted to astronomical studies, he was forced to conclude that the planets revolved around the sun. But, fearing the opposition of the Church, he refrained from publishing his findings until 1543.

The Muslims, however, did not suffer from the error of regarding as sacred that which was non-sacred. They were in a position to reflect upon matters of scientific interest with open minds, and in a purely academic way. When they found that the heliocentric theory was more rational, they accepted it without any hesitation.

Edward McNall Burns writes that the heliocentric theory developed by Aristarchus (310-230 B.C.), although destined to fall into oblivion for four hundred years, has today become an established fact. This is after many centuries of men's minds being dominated by Ptolemy's geocentric theory.

Of all the subjects developed by the Spanish Muslims, there was none brought to a higher degree of perfection than science. In fact, in this field, their successes were such as to have no parallel in history. They distinguished themselves in the fields of astronomy, mathematics, physics, chemistry, medicine, etc. As McNall Burns writes:

> Despite their reverence for Aristotle, they did not hesitate to criticize his notion of a universe of concentric spheres with the earth at the centre, and they admitted the possibility that the earth rotates on its axis and revolves around the sun.[51]

The Muslims arriving at the correct hypothesis of the solar system's functioning was made possible only because Islam had broken down the walls of conditioned thinking which had acted as a barrier to man's intellectual progress. As soon as this artificial barrier was out of the way, the caravan of human thought began to move on its journey with a hitherto unimaginable rapidity. And thus it brought us finally to the spectacular scientific feats of the present century.

MEDICINE

Just as diseases have afflicted man in every age, so has the science of medicine always existed in one form or the other. In ancient times, however, the science of medicine never reached the heights of progress that it did in the Islamic era and also latterly, in modern times.

It is believed that the beginning of the science of medicine—a beginning to be reckoned with—was made in ancient Greece. The two very great physicians who were born in ancient Greece were Hippocrates and Galen. Hippocrates lived in the fifth and fourth centuries B.C. However, very little is known about his life. The historians of later times have estimated that Hippocrates was probably born in 460 B.C. and died in 377 B.C. Some historians, on the other hand, even have doubts about his being a historical figure. It has also been questioned whether the books on philosophy and medicine supposedly written by him were not actually written by someone else and later attributed to him.[52]

Galen is considered the second most important philosopher and physicist of this period of antiquity. He was born probably in A.D. 129 and died in A.D. 199. Galen had to face stiff opposition in Rome, and most of his writings were destroyed. The remainder would also have been lost to posterity if the Arabs had not collected them in the ninth century and translated them into Arabic. These Arabic translations were later to reach Europe, in the eleventh century, where they were translated from Arabic into Latin.

The *Encyclopaedia Britannica* (1984) concludes its article on Galen: "Little is known of Galen's final years."[53]

It is a fact that ancient Greece produced some very fine brains and some very high thinking in this field. But the respective fates of Galen and Hippocrates show that the atmosphere in ancient Greece was conducive neither to the rise of such people to their due eminence, nor to the growth of medicine as a science. Different kinds of superstitious beliefs were an obstruction in the path of free enquiry; for instance, the attribution of diseases to mysterious powers, and the sanctification of many things, such as plants which had healing properties.

The science of medicine came into being in ancient Greece about 200 years before the Christian era and flourished for another two centuries. In this way, the whole period extended over about four or five hundred years. This science did not see any subsequent advance in Greece itself. Although a European country, Greece did not contribute anything to the spread of its own medical science in Europe, or to modern medicine in the West. These facts are proof that the atmosphere in ancient Greece was not favourable to the progress of medicine.

The Greek medicine which was brought into being by certain individuals (effort was all at the individual level, as the community did not give it general recognition) remained hidden away in obscure books for about one thousand years after its birth. It was only when these books were translated into Arabic during the Abbasid period (750-1258), and edited by the Arabs with their own original additions, that it became possible for this science to find its way to Europe, thus paving the way for modern medical science.

The reason for this is that before the Islamic revolution, the world had been swept by superstitious beliefs and idolatry. The environment in those times was so unfavourable that whenever an individual undertook any academic or scientific research, he could never be certain of receiving encouragement. More often than not, he had to face severe antagonism. Indeed, whenever any scientific endeavour at the individual level came to the notice of the authorities, it would be promptly and rigorously suppressed. In a situation where diseases and their remedies were tradition-ally linked with gods and goddesses, what appeal could the scientific method of treatment have for the people? Only when the monotheistic revolution came to the world in the wake of Islam did the door open to that medical progress which saw its culmination in modern medical science.

As the Prophet said, "God has sent the remedy for every disease in the world except death." This saying of the Prophet was the declaration of the leader of a revolution. No sooner did he announce to the world this truth about medicine than history began to be shaped by it in many practical ways.

ＡAMPLE

Smallpox is considered one of the most dangerous diseases in the world. It is a highly contagious disease, characterised by fever and the appearance of small spots leaving scars in the form of pits. The symptoms include chill, headache, and backache. The spots appear about the fourth day. This is a fatal disease. Even if one survives the attack, the skin is scarred permanently.

According to present records, this disease was identified in Egypt in 1122 B.C. and is also mentioned in ancient Indian books written in Sanskrit. In the past this disease gripped many countries in the form of dangerous epidemics. Thousands of people fell prey to it. As far back as 1156 B.C. this disease was taking its toll of human life, there being visible evidence in the pock-marked face of the mummy of the Egyptian Pharaoh, Ramses V, who died in that year. (His embalmed body was found inside a pyramid.) Even then, it took thousands of years for this dreaded disease to be investigated scientifically.[54]

Now we know that smallpox is a contagious disease resulting from virus infection, and such remedies have been discovered as can ward off attacks, provided suitable precautions are taken in advance.

But it was not until the end of the ninth century, subsequent to the emergence of Islam, that this medical fact was unearthed for the first time. The first name which became prominent in history in this connection was that of the well-known Arab physician, Al-Razi (865-925), who was born in Ray in Iran. In search of a remedy for the disease, he investigated it from the purely medical standpoint and wrote the first book on the subject, called, *Al-Judri wa al-Hasba*. This was translated into Latin, the academic language of ancient Europe, in 1565 in Venice. It was later translated into Greek and other European languages, and thus spread all over Europe. Its English translation, published in London in 1848, was entitled, *A Treatise on Smallpox and Measles*.

Researchers have accepted that this is the first medical book on smallpox in the whole of recorded history. Prior to this, no one had ever done research on this topic.

After reading Al-Razi's book, Edward Jenner (1749-1823), the English physician who became the inventor of vaccination, was led to making a clinical investigation of the disease. He carried on his research over a twenty-year period, ultimately establishing the connection between cowpox and smallpox. In 1796, he carried out his first practical experiment in inoculation. This was a success, and the practice spread rapidly, in spite of violent opposition from certain quarters, until, in 1977, it was announced by the UN that for the first time in history, smallpox had been eradicated.

Now the question arises as to why such a long time had elapsed between the initial discovery of the disease and the first attempts to investigate it medically with a view to finding a remedy. The reason was the prevalence of *shirk*, that is, the holding of something to be sacred when it is not, or the attribution of divinity to the non-divine.

Dr. David Werner writes, 'In most places in India, people believe that these diseases are caused because the goddess is angry with their family or their community. The goddess expresses her anger through the diseases. The people believe that the only hope of a cure for these diseases is to make offerings to her in order to please her. They do not feed the sick child or care for him because they fear this will annoy the goddess more. So the sick child becomes very weak and either dies or takes a long time to get cured. These diseases are caused by virus infection. It is essential that the child be given plenty of food to keep up his strength so that he can fight the infection.'

When Islam came to the world, it banished such superstitious beliefs about disease, announcing in no uncertain terms that none except God had the power to harm or benefit mankind. The Creator was the one and only being who had such power. All the rest were His creatures and His slaves. When, after the Islamic revolution, such ideas gained ground, people began to think freely and independently of all superstitions. Only then did it become possible to conduct medical research into disease in order to discover appropriate remedies.

Only after this intellectual revolution had come to the world did it become possible to make smallpox the subject of enquiry. Only then did it become possible for such people as Abu Bakr Razi and Edward Jenner to rise and save the world from this dreaded disease by discovering a remedy for it.

The real barrier to finding a cure was the generally accepted body of superstitious beliefs based on idol worship; these beliefs were swept away for the first time in history by Islam.

LINGUISTICS

On account of superstitious beliefs becoming attached to language, linguistics, as a science, stagnated for thousands of years. Writing of this failure to Dr Ernest Gellner, a linguist very aptly commented: 'Linguistic philosophy has an inverted vision which treats genuine thought as a disease and dead thought as a paradigm of health.'

In antiquity it was generally believed that writing was the gift of God, as in the Indian concept of "Braham lipi." Words and the forms of speech were considered to have been given to man by the gods and, as such, they commanded the highest veneration from humans. John Stevens, in his book *Sacred Calligraphy of the East,* presents research carried out by himself, which shows that the concept of 'sacred' calligraphy persisted for centuries. Scholars differed as to the origin of calligraphy, whether in Egypt, China, India, or any other place. One idea, however, was universal: writing was divine. It was inherently holy. Writing was the speech of the gods.

That human languages have been the object of superstitions for thousands of year is a matter of historical record. It was supposed that certain languages had a divine origin, and that their speakers enjoyed a special status above others. For instance, for centuries the Greek language had been supposed to be superior to other languages, Greek being the language of the gods, while other languages were those of barbarians.

The same was the case with Hebrew. In the Jewish-

Christian world it was an age-old belief that Hebrew was God's own language and that it was the first language to be used in the world. Wonderly and Eugene Nida, who have made a detailed study of the influences of Christian beliefs on languages, have made this analysis:

> One of the factors which retarded linguistic progress was the belief among early Christian writers, and persisting well into the Renaissance era, that all languages were derived from Hebrew.[55]

The concept of 'divine' language was wholly a product of superstitious beliefs, having nothing to do with reality. Whenever it comes to be supposed of a language that it is the language of the gods, it becomes an object of reverence in people's eyes with the status of a sacred language. It can no longer remain an object of investigation. After this stage, making a critical analysis of it, or advocating a new method to develop it, or any other such progressive attitude towards it, are looked upon as heretical, and akin to being sacrilegious. All such efforts are seen by the people as presumptuousness, rather than as a sincere attempt to develop the language. This state of arrested development was typical not only of the ancient languages, but of all other departments of thought, innumerable kinds of superstitious beliefs having stemmed the tide of intellectual progress. It was the revolution based on monotheism which broke down this barrier for the first time in history. This revolution originated in Arabia, and finally came to exert its influence all over the world. Human history then entered the age of realism, leaving behind the age of superstition.

The very moment when the Qur'an announced that

there was no god but the one God, the scientific way of thinking was set in motion. People began thinking about things independently of unrealistic, mental barriers. This way of thinking went from strength to strength until, finally, it led to the present scientific revolution.

The monotheistic practice of according the status of divinity to the one and only God, and denying sanctity to all else, divested all other creatures and things of any special status they may have had.

It was actually the 'divine' status of things which had been acting as a barrier to their becoming of research and investigation. Once all these things were shorn of their former so-called divinity, they naturally came down to the level of being proper subjects for research and investigation. It is this unique achievement of Islam which entitles it to be regarded as the creator of the modern age.

NUMERALS

The present system of numerals was first invented in India. That was in an age, however, when all that was traditionally established had come to be regarded as holy, while all that was invented was suspect. As such, this method of writing numerals could not become widely known, and continued for a long time to remain hidden in privately owned books. The new invention did not, therefore, gain currency: people clung to the old method, considering it to be holy.

Having learnt that in the recently established Baghdad

empire great appreciation was shown for new inventions, an Indian traveller went in 771 to Baghdad, which was then under the rule of the Abbasid Caliph, Al-Mansur. The Indian pandit introduced into Baghdad a treatise on astronomy, a *siddhanta* (the Arabs called it *sind hind*) and a treatise on mathematics. By order of Al-Mansur these books were translated into Arabic by Muhammad Ibn-Ibrahim al-Fazari, between 796 and 806. The famous Arab mathematician, Al-Khwarizmi (780-850) went through this translation into which the digit zero had been introduced. He found that with the nine Indian figures, 1-9, and the zero sign, any number could be written. Calling these the 'Indian' numerals, Al Khwarizmi pronounced them the most satisfactory, and advocated their general adoption.

Philip K. Hitti writes:

> Al Khwarizmi, writing in the first half of the ninth century, was the exponent of the use of numerals, including the zero, in preference to letters. These numerals he called Hindi, indicating their Indian origin. His work on the Hindu method of calculation was translated into Latin by Adelard of Bath in the twelfth century and as *De numero indico* has survived, whereas the Arabic original has been lost.[56]

In ancient times Roman numerals were in general use in Europe. In this system, letters were used to express numbers, a method adopted by the Greeks and some other ancient nations, and later by the Romans, who used the seven letters—M.D.C.L. X.V. I—in various combinations. For instance the figure 88 would be written as LXXXVIII. This was a cumbersome method and made calculation extremely difficult. The Europeans, however, regarded the Roman numerals as holy—a gift from the gods. As a result, they failed to revise their thinking in this matter. Regarding non-holy numerals as holy was the reason they failed to make any progress in science and mathematics for several hundred years. It was the Islamic revolution which for the first time dispelled the aura of sanctity surrounding the numeral and ushered in the era of scientific progress in Europe.

Leonardo of Pisa was the most distinguished mathematician of the Middle Ages. He helped introduce into mathematics the Hindu-Arabic numerals and the number sequence that bears his name.

Little is known about Leonardo's life beyond the few facts given in his mathematical writings. It is probable that he was born in Pisa, Italy. During Leonardo's boyhood, his father, Guglielmo, a Pisan merchant, was appointed consul, or chief magistrate, over the community of Pisan merchants in the North African port of Bugia (now Bejara, Algeria). Leonardo soon joined him. With a view to future usefulness the father sent his son to study calculation with an Arab master. Leonardo later described his enjoyment in learning the art of the nine Indian figures. Leonardo also travelled to Egypt, Syria, Greece, and Sicily, etc., where he studied different numerical systems and methods of calculation but never found one as satisfactory as the Arabic numerals.

When Leonardo's *Liber abaci* first appeared, Arabic numerals were known to only a few European intellectuals through translation of the writings of the ninth century Arab mathematician and astronomer Al-Khwarizmi. Leonardo began his explanation of the notation by observing: "The nine Arabic figures are; 9 8 7 6 5 4 3 2 1. With these nine figures and with the sign 0... any number may be written, as is demonstrated below." The first seven chapters dealt with the notation, explaining the principle of place value, by which the position of a figure determines whether it is a unit, ten, hundred and so forth, and demonstrating the use of the numerals in arithmetical operations. The techniques were then applied to such practical commercial problems as profit margin, barter, money changing, conversion of weights, partnerships, and interest.

The *Liber abaci,* which was widely copied and imitated, drew the attention of the Holy Roman Emperor, Frederick II, who was a patron of science. In the year 1220, Leonardo was invited to appear before the Emperor at Pisa, and there he propounded a series of problems, three of which Leonardo presented in his books. The first two belonged to a favourite Arabic type.

Wilfrid Blunt writes:

> And supposing the tide of Islam had not been stemmed? Nothing so delayed the advance of science in the West as the clumsiness of the Roman numerals. Had the Arabic numerals, which had reached Baghdad from India towards the end of the eighth century, been soon afterwards introduced into and adopted by western Europe as a whole, much of that scientific progress which we associate with the Renaissance in Italy might have been achieved several centuries earlier.[57]

AN EXPLANATION

For those who are interested in how the concept of zero

originated in India, the Children's Book Trust, New Delhi has published a 22 page booklet in English entitled, 'The Story of Zero,' which has been written for the general reader as well as for children by Dilip M. Salwai.

Before this invention there existed no simple method of representing large figures. According to one method, certain words were fixed for particular figures like Sahasara for 1,000, Aayota for 10,000, Laksha for 100,000, and Koti for 1,000,000. The invention of zero revolutionized the science of mathematics, for now it became extremely easy to denote large figures.

Brahma Gupta (598-660), who was born in Multan, was the first notable person to work out a method of using the zero. However his method had some shortcomings. Later on Bhaskar (1114-1185), who was born in Bijapur, wrote a book in Sanskrit called *Lailawati*, in which he described the zero concept in simpler and more understandable terms.

R. K. Murthi, in his review of this book, writes: "It boosts our sense of national pride to note that the zero was conceived of in India."[58]

The writer of *Lailawati* tells us that "the Indian numbers first entered Spain, then Italy, France, England and Germany... Indian numbers were accepted completely.... Their adoption turned out to be the turning point in the history of mathematics and science."[59]

It is true that the concept of zero originated in India, but it is not true that it reached the western world directly from India: it was through the Arabs that it reached the

West. That is why the West calls these numerals Arabic rather than Indian. The *Encyclopaedia Britannica* says:

> Arabic numerals—the numbers, o 1, 2, 3, 4, 5, 6, 7, 8, 9 they may have originated in India, but were introduced to the western world from Arabia.[60]

The *Encyclopaedia* tells us, moreover, that these numbers became known to western intellectuals in the ninth century through the writings of the Arab mathematician, Al-Khwarizmi, whose explanations of numbers in Arabic reached Europe through Latin translations.[61]

Bertrand Russell writes:

> About 830, Muhammad ibn Musa al-Khwarizmi, a translator of mathematical and astronomical books from the Sanskrit, published a book which was translated into Latin in the twelfth century, under the title *Algorimi de numero Indrum*. It was from this book that the west first learnt of what we call 'Arabic' numerals, which ought to be called 'Indian.' The same author wrote a book on algebra which was used in the West as a text-book until the sixteenth century.[62]

In spite of the concept of zero having originated in India, for several hundred years it received no recognition in India itself. It came to be generally known in India only when first the Arabs and then the West adopted it. The *Encyclopaedia Britannica* says: "The invention, probably by the Hindus, of the digit zero, has been described as one of the greatest importance in the history of mathematics. Hindu literature gives evidence that the zero may have been known before the birth of Christ, but no inscription has been found with such a symbol before the ninth century."[63]

It is true then that the concept of zero had first formed in the mind of an Indian. But at that period in history, India was dominated wholly by polytheism and superstition. Everything was shrouded in mystery and inventions were abhorred. That was why the concept of zero did not receive general recognition in ancient India. It was reduced to a mere discovery of an individual, and thus failed to win general approval. The seed of India, neglected at home, did, however, fall on fertile soil in Muslim Baghdad, where it flowered into a tree and then, via Muslim Spain, spread all over Europe.

Yet, without Islam having first put an end to the concepts of polytheism and superstition, the concept of zero—like so many other innovative ideas—could not have been universally welcomed.

AGRICULTURE

The river was one of those phenomena of nature held to possess divine attributes. People believed that therein dwelt a mysterious spirit which caused the water to move and made it useful or harmful.[64]

The river Skamandros in ancient Greece evidently was so personified, according to Aeshines, a fourth century B.C. Greek orator. Girls bathed in it before marrying and said: "Skamandros, accept my virginity." Magical rites in which water serves as a substitute for semen or the fertility of men are numerous.[65]

Because rivers were held to be sacred in ancient times

(even to this day, some are still held sacred) people began to worship them and offer up sacrifices to them. It was this concept of holiness that hindered man in his conquest of nature. People saw rivers in the form of deities rather than in the form of physical objects to be exploited by common methods. That is why the use of river water in agriculture remained limited in antiquity. It is astonishing that the history of irrigation had its beginnings in relatively modern times.

With the onset of the Islamic revolution based on monotheism, it was revealed to man that the river was a creature and not a creator, it was a servant and not the Lord. Only then was it possible for man to give thought to finding ways and means to exploit rivers on a large scale. That is why we come across the fact in history books that there is no precedent in any nation to the large-scale irrigation system developed by the Spanish Muslims.

The Spanish Muslims developed agriculture to such an extent that it became a regular science. They studied trees and carried out research on the properties of soil. Vast expanses of land which had hitherto been lying infertile were then converted into orchards and lush green fields. It was a virtual green revolution.

Philip K. Hitti writes:

> They dug canals, cultivated grapes and introduced among other plants and fruits, rice, apricots, peaches, pomegranates, oranges, sugarcane, cotton and saffron. The south-eastern plains of the peninsula, especially favoured by climate and soil, developed important centres of rural and urban activity. Here wheat and

other grains as well as olives and sundry fruits were raised by a peasantry who worked the soil on shares with the owners.

The agricultural development was one of the glories of Moslem Spain and one of the Arabs' lasting gifts to the land, for Spanish gardens have preserved to this day a "Moorish" imprint. One of the best-known gardens is the Generalife (from *Al-Janat al-arif*, the inspector's paradise), a Nasrid monument of the late thirteenth century whose villa was one of the outlying buildings of the Alhambra. This garden, proverbial for its extensive shade, falling waters and soft breeze, was terraced in the form of an amphitheatre and irrigated by streams which, after forming numerous cascades, lost themselves among the flowers, shrubs and trees represented today by a few gigantic cypresses and myrtles.[66]

Charles Sinobose, a French author, writes that the Spanish Arabs adopted the method of irrigation by canals. They also dug large wells. Those who discovered new sources of water were given sizeable rewards. In Spain they dug broad canals, and then subdivided them, with the result that the arid plain of Valencia was turned into a vast tract of lush green. They established a permanent department of irrigation which supplied all kinds of relevant information.

Describing Muslim Spain, Bertrand Russell writes:

One of the best features of the Arab economy was agriculture, particularly the skillful use of irrigation, which they learnt from living where water is scarce. To this day Spanish agriculture profits by Arab irrigation works.[67]

It is a fact that the Muslims who went to Spain brought about a veritable green revolution. There they established such irrigation systems for fields and orchards as were unprecedented in history. However, strangely enough,

Bertrand Russell attributes this to their having lived in the past in desert areas, where water is scarce. This explanation is meaningless. The true, underlying cause of this feat is the monotheistic revolution which had overhauled the minds of Arabs. Prior to this, people had seen rivers, springs, and the sea in the form of gods. They held them to be objects of reverence rather than of conquest. The Arabs with their changed mind saw these phenomena of nature in the form of God's creations. They saw them with an eye to conquering them for exploitation. It was this mental revolution which enabled the Arabs to perform their historic feats in the world of irrigation and agriculture.

How can we learn methods of irrigation in the desert where water is scarce? Ignorant of the true source of this Arab skill, Bertrand Russell linked it, quite irrelevantly, to their life in the desert, sans water, instead of to their mental revolution which had come about thanks to monotheism. The science of irrigation was developed not because of their desert life but because of their monotheistic thinking.

HISTORIOGRAPHY

The starting point in Arnold Toynbee's philosophy of history was his contention that the proper unit of historical study must be a civilization, rather than the traditional unit, the nation state.[68]

Both these concepts, however, hinge on the same principle: that history should not focus solely on royal actions and prerogatives throughout the ages, but should be a study of the sum of all activities of all groups of human beings, whatever the framework, political or civilizational, within which they interact. In the long history of mankind, this approach, developed only during the last few centuries, is relatively new. History, or historiography, is now equated with 'man-story' as opposed to the 'King-story' of the pre-modern era. 'King-story,' made up of elaborate descriptions of kings, along with copious details of the palaces they occupied and the generals they commanded, had made no mention of the common man, even if his achievements were marked by greatness. The only man considered worthy of mention was the one whose head was adorned by a crown. Ancient history thus amounted to a belittling of humanity in general.

While real events relating to non-kings were regarded as undeserving of any mention, even legendary tales and concocted stories about the kings were preserved in writing as if they were great realities. Take, for instance, the building of Alexandria, the renowned coastal city named after its founder, Alexander the Great. Many strange stories are associated with the foundation of this city. One of them concerns sea genies who were said to have put obstacles in the path of building when the work was first started. Alexander, so the story goes, decided to see for himself what the genies were about. He gave orders for a large box of wood and glass to be made, and when it was ready, he had himself lowered in it to the bottom of the sea. There he drew pictures of the genies and then back on land, he had metal statues cast to look exactly like the dragons. These statues were then laid under the foundations of Alexandria. When the sea genies came there, and saw that genies like themselves had been killed and buried in the foundations, they became frightened and ran away. The fact that this tale gained currency shows the credulous state in which the whole world lived before the advent of Islam.

In old historical records, the most striking omissions are the lives and influence of the great prophets of the world. Today, people would find it very strange if a history of the freedom struggle of India laid no stress on the role of Gandhiji, or if a history of the erstwhile U.S.S.R. omitted Lenin altogether. But a far strange history is one bereft of all mention of those pious souls, who were the messengers of God. The sole exception to this rule of omission is the Final Prophet, the Prophet Muhammad ﷺ. The reason for his prominent inclusion in historical records is that, by setting in motion the Islamic revolution, he was able to change exactly those factors—the undemocratic, polytheistic and superstitious nature of society—which in the past had been responsible for such astonishing lacunae in the writing of human history. There can be no doubt that it was the Islamic revolution which made it possible for historiography to proceed on scientific lines.

In known human history, Ibn Khaldun (1332-1406) is the only historian to have changed the pattern of historiography. It was he who raised historiography from the level of mere King-story to the level of genuine man-story. "Kingology" was changed into sociology. The truth is that the science known today as sociology is the gift of Ibn Khaldun. He himself claimed that he was the founder of sociology, and there is no reason to dispute his claim.

Khaldun's greatness was acknowledged in a similar vein by Robert Flint: "As a theorist on history he had no equal in any age or country until Vico appeared, more than three hundred years later; Plato, Aristotle and Augustine were not his peers."[69]

It was indeed Ibn Khaldun who gave to Europe the modern science of history. And it was Islam which bestowed this gift upon him. The Islamic revolution produced Ibn Khaldun and Ibn Khaldun produced the modern science of history.

Professor Philip K. Hitti writes:

> The fame of Ibn-Khaldun rests on his Muqaddama (Introduction to his book on history). In it he presented for the first time a theory of historical development which takes due cognizance of the physical facts of climate and geography as well as of the moral and spiritual forces at work. As one who endeavoured to formulate laws of national progress and decay, Ibn Khaldun may be considered the discoverer—as he himself claimed—of the true scope and nature of history, or at least the real founder of the science of sociology. No Arab writer, indeed no European, had ever taken a view of history at once so comprehensive and philosophic. By the consensus of critical opinion Ibn-Khaldun was the greatest historical philosopher Islam produced, and one of the greatest of all time.
>
> In Book I of the Muqaddamah, Ibn Khaldun sketches a general sociology; in Books II and III, a sociology of politics; in Book IV a sociology of urban life; in Book V, a sociology of economics; and in Book VI, a sociology of knowledge. The work is studded with brilliant observations on historiography, economics, politics,

and education. It is held together by his central concept of *asabiyah*, or social cohesion. Thus he laid the foundation of a science of history which is not based just on the description of kings, but which is, in a vaster sense, based on the economics, politics, education, religion, ethics, and culture of the whole nation.[70]

Historians have generally acknowledged that the science of history remained undeveloped before the emergence of Ibn Khaldun, and that he was the first person to develop a philosophy of history. The *Encyclopaedia Britannica* even goes so far as to say that "he developed one of the world's most significant philosophies of history."[71]

The question arises as to how it became possible for Ibn Khaldun to discover something which had remained undiscovered for centuries. The answer is that other historians were born before the Islamic revolution, while Ibn Khaldun was born after it. On the basis of monotheism, Islam had brought about a revolution which eliminated the difference between King and commoner. All human beings, the offspring of Adam and Eve, were held to be equal. It was, uniquely, this great revolution of equality that paved the way for an Ibn Khaldun—himself a product of this revolution—to lay the foundation of modern history in which the central position was held not by 'royal figures' but by humanity itself.

One belief which had hampered the development of the science or art of history was polytheism. The whole period prior to Islam was pervaded by polytheistic beliefs which were supportive of divine kingship. "The King has often stood as mediator between his people and their god, or as the god's representative."[72] Some kings pretended to be incarnations of God, or even gods themselves, without feeling the need to rationalize their claims. They did so in order that by the 'divine right of kings,' their absolute sovereignty should never be questioned. Even where monarchs made no such claims, they were credited with divinity, because divinity was universally associated with kings. Whenever the common people came upon anything that was out of the ordinary, they regarded it as supernatural and, if it was a person, they took him to be a god, or a manifestation of a god. Naturally, this mentality was not discouraged by the kings.

The ancient rulers, on the contrary, encouraged such superstitious notions so that people would continue to regard them as superior beings. In known history, the Prophet Muhammad, upon whom be peace, was the first ruler who refuted such superstitious beliefs, showing them to be without foundation. In this way, he lead mankind along the path of enlightenment, eliminating the differences between men on an intellectual plane. He held as baseless all those suppositions and superstitions which had been responsible for creating and perpetuating the slave-master mentality.

Towards the end of the Prophet Muhammad's life, Maria Qibtiya bore him a beautiful and vivacious son in Medina. The Prophet named him Ibrahim, after the Prophet Abraham ﷺ. Ibrahim was just one and a half years old when, in the tenth year of Hijrah (January 632 A.D.), he died. It so happened that the death of Ibrahim coincided with a solar eclipse. From ancient times, one of the many prevailing superstitions was that the solar and lunar eclipses were caused by the death of some king or other important personage. They were meant to show, they thought, that the heavens mourned the death of the exalted in station. At that time the Prophet Muhammad ﷺ was King of Arabia. For this reason, certain of the Medinans began attributing the eclipse to the death of the Prophet's son. As soon as the Prophet heard of this, he refuted it. There are several accounts of this incident in the books of Hadith. One of these was recorded as follows:

> One day the Prophet came in great haste to the mosque. At that time the sun was in eclipse. The Prophet began to say his prayers and, by the time he had finished, the eclipse was over. Then, addressing the congregation, he said that people imagined that the sun and moon went into eclipse at the death of some important person, but that this was not true. The eclipses of the sun and moon were not due to the death of any human being. Both the sun and the moon were just two of God's creations, with which He did as He willed. He told them that when they saw an eclipse, they should pray to God.[73]

When the whole of Arabia had come under the domination of Islam, the Prophet made a farewell Hajj pilgrimage in his last days, along with 125,000 companions. During this pilgrimage he delivered his historic sermon on the plain of 'Arafat which is known as *Khutba Hajjatul Wida*, the sermon of the farewell pilgrimage.

This sermon was a declaration of human rights: "Hear, O people. All human beings are born of a man and a woman. All the apparent differences are only for the sake of introduction and identification. The most worthy before God is the one who is the most God-fearing. No Arab has any superiority over a non-Arab and vice versa. No black has any superiority over a white and vice versa. *Taqwa* (piety) is the only thing which will determine one's superiority over others." To this the Prophet added, "All things of the period of ignorance before Islam have been trampled down by my steps." For the first time in ancient history, all sorts of inequality and discrimination were almost entirely eliminated.

Only then did a new civilization come into being in which all human beings were equal. Speaking of the successors of the Prophet, Abu Bakr and ʿUmar, Mahatma Gandhi noted that "though they were masters of a vast empire, they lived the life of paupers."

This revolution was so powerful that even at a later period, when the rot had set in in the institutions of governments, and the Caliphs had been replaced by "emperors," the pressure of Islamic civilization was so great that none of these "emperors" could live in the style of the ancient monarchs. In Islamic history there are many such instances. The following incident, which took place during the reign of Sultan Abdur Rahman II (A.D. 176–258), a powerful ruler of Muslim Spain, is an apt illustration.

This Sultan had a palace built for himself called az-Zahra, to the east of Cordova, which was of such immensity that the word palace was not adequate to describe it. This magnificent residence came to be known as *al-Madinah az-Zahirah* (the brilliant town). But, in spite of being so powerful and living in such magnificence, the Sultan did not regard himself as being above the law.

It happened once that he missed one fast in the month of Ramazan without having any excuse which would be acceptable in terms of the *shari'ah*. He therefore assembled the *'ulama* (religious scholars) of Cordova, and told them of his lapse. He asked them to pronounce a religious verdict which would enable him to atone for it.

Al-Maqqari writes that one of the religious scholars present was Imam Yahya, who promptly decreed that the King should observe 60 continuous fasts in expiation. On leaving the palace, he was asked by one of the 'Ulama why he had insisted on such a severe form of punishment when the *shari'ah* offered the alternative of feeding 60 poor people in atonement for one missed fast. Why had he not instructed the King to feed 60 poor people instead of requiring him to fast himself?

Angered by this question, Imam Yahya replied, "For a king to feed 60 poor people is no punishment." As we learn from the annals of Andalusion history, Sultan Abdur Rahman II did accept the *fatwa* (verdict) of Imam Yahya, and did observe 60 continuous fasts. He showed no reaction whatsoever. He did not even dismiss Imam Yahya from his office.[74]

This can be explained in terms of the impact of the Islamic revolution, which had put an end to the difference between a subject and a ruler. It had created such an atmosphere of human equality, that no one could regard himself as being superior to others. Not even a king dared to set himself apart from the commoners or to flout the law.

Before the Islamic revolution it was an accepted fact that the king was superior to a common man. For instance, the Byzantine emperor, Heraclius, a contemporary of the Prophet Muhammad ﷺ, in spite of being a Christian, "had married his niece, Martina, thus offending the religious scruples of many of his subjects, who viewed his second marriage as incestuous."[75]

It was known to the people that this marriage was illegal, yet there was no public outcry. This was because Heraclius was a king and, therefore, above any judgement by human standards. As a king, he had the right to do as he pleased.

In ancient times, this extraordinary concept of the greatness of kings was so firmly implanted, as a matter of superstitious belief, that ordinary citizens had begun to consider their monarchs to be innately superior creatures. The observance of special rites and rituals by kings was aimed at reinforcing this way of thinking. The kings had thus, in their respective empires, achieved a temporal greatness which was on a parallel with God's prerogative in the vastness of His universe. It was but natural that historiography should come under the influence of this concept of the 'divine right of the kings' so that, in practice, it became a chronicle of the lives of royal families with scant reference to the common man.

With the onset of the Islamic revolution in Arabia and neighbouring countries, objects of nature like the sun and moon were dislodged from their divine pedestals. In like manner, kings were removed from the seat of extraordinary greatness. Now a king was just a human being like any other.

The influence of the Islamic revolution, which ultimately reached Asia, Africa and many European countries, paved the way for a new atmosphere on a universal scale. With the new way of thinking, the old king-centred mentality gave way to a man-centred ethos. Prominent expression was given to a new approach to historiography in the writings of Abdur Rahman Ibu Khaldun, who in the foreword to his *Kitab al- Ibar,* propounded his theory of how history should be written. This foreword, or *Muqaddamah,* is considered so important that it has been published many times in several languages.

The most eminent of the Mamluk historians was al-Maqrizi, a disciple of Ibn Khaldun. It was through him in the fifteenth century that Ibn Khaldun's theories were introduced into Egypt. Later, other Muslim countries came under their influence. Between 1860 and 1870 a complete rendering of the *Muqaddamah* was published in French, thus introducing his historical theories into Europe. These thoughts took root in the soil of Europe, and gained great popularity. Vico and other western historians developed this art, finally giving rise to the modern form of historiography.

4

Liberty, Equality, Fraternity

One of the most cherished dreams of philosophers and thinkers has always been the brotherhood of equality. The Prophet of Islam, however, was the first person to bring about a revolution which, for the first time in history, actually established equality in practice. This has been generally acknowledged by serious scholars. For instance, in his letter No. 175, Swami Vivekanand wrote that in his experience, "if ever any religion approached to this equality in an appreciable manner, it is Islam and Islam alone."[76]

If, throughout history, equality in practice had been the exception to the rule, it was because of the general acceptance of polytheism, which had proved a stumbling block to many other kinds of progress throughout the ages. Whereas the domination of polytheism had perpetuated inequality among human beings, the domination of monotheism now established human equality.

The truth is that, in temperament and physique, human beings display many differences, be they inherited or acquired. For instance, one is black, another white, one is rich, another poor, one rules, another is ruled. These differences exist, according to the Qur'an, as a matter of identification (49:13) and for the sake of differentiating one from another and not for the purpose of discrimination. One might put it that these differences are a matter of classification, so that the world may be properly organized. This does not mean then that some are of high, while others are of low status. These differences exist only to facilitate the structuring of the activities of a world which exhibits so great a diversity.

Just as man had formed unrealistic concepts regarding physical phenomena under the influence of superstitions born of polytheistic beliefs, similarly, unrealistic concepts about human beings also gained universal currency. Over the centuries, these concepts came to form part of the traditions of the peoples of the world. For instance, it was this concept of inequality which led to the formation of the caste system in certain societies. It was believed that some people were born of the head of God, whilst others sprang from His feet. As such, they were divided into high and low castes. In a similar way, the concept was formed of the kings being the offspring of the gods, with the common people there only to serve them. In many societies, the concept was formed of some being superior, and others being inferior, by birth, or by race.

Discriminatory practices, based on the concept of inequality, had become prevalent under the influence of polytheism and, over the centuries, had come to be a permanent feature of human history. It even came to be believed that just as the night is destined to be dark and the day to be bright, similarly the division of human beings on the above-mentioned bases could never ever be brought to an end. It was something which had existed and always would exist eternally—that being the will of the gods.

The domination of polytheism and superstition had to be overcome in order to usher in the age of equality. But even with the advent of thousands of prophets, it could not be brought into existence. For the Prophet Muhammad ﷺ, being the last of the prophets, it became absolutely imperative to terminate, once and for all, the domination of superstitious beliefs. In theory, each of the prophets in turn had demolished such beliefs, but, in practice, people's personal interests had kept them alive, so that superstition had not in fact been overthrown. God had, therefore, to send His special succour to the Prophet Muhammad ﷺ, who, along with his companions, then brought about the intellectual revolution which universally uprooted such dogmas. It was at that stage that the concept of inequality was rooted out forever.

In the address the Prophet made on the occasion of his last pilgrimage, he had this to say on the subject of ending polytheistic beliefs:

> No Arab has superiority over a non–Arab and no non–Arab has superiority over an Arab. No black man has superiority over a red and no red over a black. All are born of Adam and Adam was born of the earth.[77]

This declaration made by the Prophet was not just a sermon, unenforced by authority. It had the force of an official decree issued by the government of that time. It was not just a verbal injunction about 'what should be done' but was actual information about an already existing state of affairs. Its promulgation was meant not only to alert the ignorant but to reinforce a social condition. All the artificial walls dividing humanity had crumbled. A new age had been ushered in in which there was no high or low status, and no discrimination. It was an age in which one's status in society would be determined by character and achievement, and not by accidents of birth, or membership of a particular race.

A HAPPENING

In former times, when a man was discriminated against in society, he could not raise his voice, as he believed it was the result of his fate. That is, he believed himself fated from birth to have that type of treatment meted out to him. But during the rule of ʿUmar ibn al-Khattab (the second Caliph of Islam) an incident took place which showed how the times had changed. Egypt had been conquered at that period by the Muslims, and ʿAmr Ibn al-ʿAs had been appointed as its governor. One day a young Egyptian, a Copt, came before the Caliph with the complaint that the son of the Muslim governor had given him a whipping, all the while saying, "Take that! I am the son of a nobleman!" The only reason for this shameless conduct on his part was that the young Copt's horse had beaten his own horse in a race. Now, the boy, knowing of the egalitarianism brought about by the Islamic revolution, had come to the Caliph to seek justice.

The Caliph immediately sent a special emissary to Egypt to bring Amr ibn al-ʿAs and his son without delay to Medina, the capital. When they arrived, they were both brought before the Caliph. Then the latter sent for the young Copt and asked him if this was the man who had beaten him. When the Copt replied in the affirmative, the Caliph handed him a whip and asked him to flog this 'son of a nobleman.' The Copt did so, and went on flogging him till he felt that justice had been done. Then the Caliph asked him also to flog ʿAmr ibn al-ʿAs, the father of the young wrongdoer, as it had been his high status—as ʿUmar explained—which had encouraged the son to take his whip to him. But then the Copt said, "No, I have whipped the person who whipped me, and I wish no more than that."

Then the Caliph, addressing the governor, said, "O ʿAmr, since when have you enslaved people who were born free?"

The revolution brought about by the Prophet Muhammad ﷺ and his companions caused the barriers of discrimination to be swept away, all over the world. It saw the birth of a new age of human equality which ultimately developed into modern democracy.

The states of former times were founded upon polytheistic beliefs. The people worshipped the sun and the moon, and the rulers convinced the people that they were the offspring of these gods. People called the *Suraj bansi* (the sun's offspring) and the *Chandar bansi* (the moon's offspring) still survive in India. The rulers naturally wanted the people to continue to adhere to such superstitious beliefs, even to the point of believing that the sun and moon went into eclipse when the king died, for, so long as they firmly cherished such beliefs, the kings could rule over them untrammeled by any fear of an uprising.

In this way, the rulers of antiquity had become staunch patrons of polytheism and superstition. When the Prophet, with his authority as ruler, announced that eclipses of the sun and the moon were purely physical happenings, and were certainly not expressions of the greatness of particular human beings, this age-old reverence for natural objects and superstitious beliefs very soon disappeared. A new age commenced in which attribution of divine qualities to mere things existing in the world around us gave way to realistic, or in modern parlance, scientific thinking.

But, this is not all that humanity had bestowed upon it by the Prophet Muhammad ﷺ. In addition to this, there was the divine book which laid emphasis on the fact that all the things of the earth and the heavens had been subjugated, by God's will, for the benefit of mankind (Qur'an, 31:20). This was what induced people to think that rather than bow before them, imagining them to be superior to man, they should harness them to meet human requirements.

THE CREATION OF THE NEW WORLD.

The religion brought by the Prophet Muhammad ﷺ was

accepted throughout the length and breadth of Arabia. Later, it began spreading with astonishing rapidity, until, within the span of a century, it had conquered Asia and Africa, finally reaching Europe. Leaving aside the continent of America, all the countries and all the seas and oceans of the world came, directly or indirectly, under the influence of the followers of this religion.

This process continued for a thousand years. From the Sukutu Caliphate of Nigeria to the Muslim Sultanates of Indonesia, and from the Ottoman empire of Turkey to the Mughal empire of India, there existed one vast expanse of the globe where national and geographical boundaries, such as we have in modern times, were simply not known. Muslims, without any difficulty, could travel through this whole region for education, commerce and other purposes.

It was in this period, in the fourteenth century, that Ibn Batuta, the well-known traveller of the Middle Ages, covered about 75 thousand miles in the course of his journeying. He was able to go from one country to another without any feeling of being a stranger, and nowhere did he face the problem of unemployment. He came to India in the reign of Muhammad ibn Tughlaq (1325-51) where he was received with honours and gifts, and later appointed Grand Qadi (Judge) of Delhi.[78]

It was as a result of this universal revolution that all human beings could now be said to belong to one vast human brotherhood, a concept which rapidly came to dominate thinking all over the world. It first dominated the society of Medina, then it formed its centre in Damascus, from which point it reached Baghdad. From Spain it reached Sicily, and then went on to other European countries.

Although the greater part of Europe did not accept the Islamic concept of monotheism in respect of religion, it did, however, apply it to the universe—a revolution in thought which it fully exploited. The scientific and democratic revolution of Europe might be termed the "secular edition" of the monotheistic revolution of Islam. As this phrase implies, the West has separated the religious and secular aspects of the Islamic revolution.

The situation being such, it would be no exaggeration to say that if Islam were to be deleted from human history, all social and human progress should have to be deleted along with it. The world would then fall back into the Dark Ages where it lay for so long in intellectual shackles before the Islamic revolution came to bring it enlightenment.

FREEDOM OF THOUGHT

In ancient times, civil liberties did not include freedom of thought. Censorship, in varying degrees of rigorousness, has, in fact, been a worldwide phenomenon in all periods of history. And whether communities have been large or small has made no difference. *The Encyclopaedia of Religion and Ethics* devotes no less than 25 pages to showing, under the heading of 'persecution.' how at all stages of ancient history, people all over the world have been denied this basic freedom. "Ancient society was essentially intolerant" (p. 743). This meant that the thinking of the common man had, of necessity, to bow to the thinking of the ruling classes.

The *Encyclopaedia Britannica* also devotes eight pages to the intellectual censorship which was universally prevalent in antiquity. As a case in point, it cites the notorious example of how Chinese citizens were denied freedom of thought by Shin Huang Ti, the Emperor who built the Great Wall of China. In the year 213, he ordered all books to be burnt, saving those dealing with harmless subjects such as medicine and agriculture. Five hundred scholars were executed and thousands were banished. The punishment for failure to burn proscribed books within 30 days was branding and condemnation to forced labour.[79]

Other peoples who suffered similar oppression were the Spartans, and the early Romans, Jews and Christians. According to Plutarch, in *The Ancient Customs of the Spartans*, the Spartans learned to read and write for purely practical reasons, and all other educational influences—books and treatises as well as meetings with learned men—were banned. The arts and philosophy flourished in democratic Athens, but many artists and philosophers, among them Aeschylus, Euripides, Phidias, Socrates, and Aristotle, were exiled, imprisoned, executed, or took flight.[80]

The office of Censor was established in Rome in 443 B.C. Criticism of the Roman authorities was akin to treason. The article says, "Treason included allusion, statement, and criticism. Philosophers and rhetoricians were twice banished by law, and the political rights of actors were curtailed by edicts of the censors. Many prominent citizens were persecuted for having made critical comments on the ruling class."[81]

For almost three centuries after Christ, the Jews and Christians remained hostile to one another only because of differences in their religious beliefs. First the Jews persecuted the Christians. When in the fourth century Christianity became the religion of the empire, Christian officials persecuted the Jews.[82]

One reason for the constraint on freedom of thought in the past was that an atmosphere of intellectual freedom would have jeopardized the whole social hierarchy, based as it was on religions which had been tainted by human interpolations. Had free enquiry been fostered, the rulers would have been unable to maintain the veracity of such man-made beliefs as served their purpose. Those who attempted free and scientific enquiry in the sixteenth and seventeenth centuries in Europe were, therefore, subjected by the Church to severe persecution. It was fear on the part of the religious authorities of being overthrown which led to the persecution of these would-be scientists. Drapier has given details of these persecutions in his book entitled *Conflict between Science and Religion*. A more precise title would have been, 'Conflict between Science and Christianity.'

HUMAN INEQUALITY

Thinking, in ancient times, was heavily blinkered by polytheism. This was because it suited the rulers to have their subjects believe that the beings who occupied the thrones of this world were, in essence, different from ordinary human beings; that, in fact, kings were possessed of divine attributes. In that way, the common people remained their subjects, while they themselves enjoyed the status not just of great lords, but of divinities.

It was such polytheistic, or superstitious beliefs which had barred the way to freedom of thought. It was taken for granted that the judgement of the king was the only possible judgement and that it must, therefore, be right. No one was privileged to form independent opinions, and if others were allowed to speak, it was only to corroborate the royal views. It was such restrictive practices based on erroneous beliefs which were responsible for the stifling of freedom of thought in ancient times.

With the advent of Islam in the seventh century, however, it was declared for the benefit of mankind that all greatness was the exclusive prerogative of God, and that in the eyes of God, all human beings were equal. The Prophet Muhammad ﷺ declared not once, but on many occasions and in different ways that all were alike, all were brothers.

This, in religious terminology, is known as monotheism. The Prophet not only stated the truth, but also made it a reality by bringing about a total revolution based on the idea of human equality. In the first phase of his prophethood, his advocacy of this theory was purely verbal. But on achieving political domination in Arabia, he was able to put this theory into practice in his capacity as ruler of a state. In this way, Islam put an end to discrimination between human beings on the basis of race, colour, status, etc. People were then assigned a high or low status according to their moral worth.

FREEDOM OF EXPRESSION

The revolution set in motion by Islam on the basis of monotheism brought into existence for the first time in human history a truly egalitarian social structure. It paved the way for a society in which everyone enjoyed freedom of expression with no constraints whatsoever. Nothing of this nature had ever hitherto been experienced. Let us compare this with the human condition under Chosroes I, the Persian emperor who ruled the Sassanid empire from 531 to 579. Chosroes I was known as one of the just rulers of Persia, but even during his reign, a courtier was once bludgeoned to death in the Court at the instance of the King simply for having dared to criticize the royal policy. Such a punishment was not an exception. Any criticism or difference of opinion amounted to treason. In fact, the mildest punishment for this crime was instant execution.

Not only did Islam advocate freedom of thought and speech with unmistakable earnestness, but it also wrought such social changes as emboldened the people to break with ancient practices, thus enabling them to openly express their differences with and criticism of their chiefs and rulers.

The Prophet Muhammad 🕌 may have had the status of a political ruler in Arabia, but still he lived like any other ordinary man, and everyone was free to express himself in his presence. One such instance occurred on the Badr expedition. During the journey, the Prophet decided to encamp at a particular place. At that point a man by the name of Khabbab ibn al-Mundhir approached him and asked, "Have you chosen to halt here because you were guided by divine revelation, or is this choice of halting place purely a matter of your own private opinion?" The Prophet replied, "I have chosen this place myself." At this, Khabbab ibn al-Mundhir said, "This is no place to halt. Move from here with all your companions." The Prophet, far from rebuking the man for this audacity, simply asked him why he thought they should camp elsewhere. When he had heard his reasons, he immediately agreed with him, and he and his companions then set off to find another halting place. The fact that neither the Prophet nor his companions took exception to Khabbab ibn al-Mundhir's behaviour is a clear illustration of the degree to which egalitarianism was encouraged by Islam. (Details of this incident are available in the books on *Sirah*, the Prophet Muhammad's biography.)

This revolution, imbued as it was with the spirit of Islamic monotheism, was so powerful that its effects continued to be felt throughout the whole of Islamic history. After the Prophet, during the period of the pious caliphs, anyone, irrespective of his social status, could freely criticize the caliphs. The history of this period abounds in such instances.

This Islamic revolution had such far-reaching effects, that even in the later period of Islam, when a form of monarchy had replaced the Caliphate, and throughout the entire

fourteen-hundred-year span of Islamic history, there was
never again a ruler who succeeded in placing curbs on the
right to expression.

SOME INSTANCES OF RELIGIOUS TOLERANCE

The Islamic revolution brought about by the Prophet
and his companions did not remain simply a matter of
religion, for the followers of Islam established powerful states
far beyond the boundaries of Arabia—a process which
continued for a thousand years and affected the whole
inhabited world of that time. But never once, throughout
that period, was there any attempt to impose censorship on
human thinking. In all these new Islamic states, the people
enjoyed total freedom of thought. Here we shall quote some
instances to this effect from Professor Arnold's book, titled,
The Preaching of Islam. First, there is an excerpt from a full
statement made by one of the Spanish Muslims who had
been driven out of his native country. Protesting against the
persecution of the Inquisition, he stresses, in contrast, the
toleration of his co-religionists: "...Our arms, it is true, are
ever open to receive all who are disposed to embrace our
religion, but we are not allowed by our sacred Qur'an to
tyrannise over consciences..."[83]

Then, on the subject of the religious tolerance of the
Turks, Professor Arnold has this to say: "... at least for two
centuries after their conquest of Greece (the Ottomon
emperors) exhibit a toleration such as was at that time quite
unknown in the rest of Europe."[84] Macarius, Patriarch of
Antioch in the seventeenth century, prayed for the Turks

when he saw the fearful atrocities that the Catholic Poles inflicted on the Russians of the Orthodox Eastern Church. These are his words: "God perpetuate the empire of the Turks for ever and ever! For they take their impost, and enter into no account of religion, be their subjects Christians or Nazarenes, Jews or Samarians."[85]

Giving many further instances of the freedom of thought and expression during the Muslim period, Arnold has written that those Roman provinces which were rapidly conquered by Muslims suddenly found themselves in such an atmosphere of tolerance as had been unknown to them for centuries. Such tolerance was quite striking in the history of the seventh century.

RELIGIOUS FREEDOM

Professor Arnold mentions another incident which took place during the rule of the Abbasid Caliph, al-Mamun (813–33). When al-Mamun came to know that the enemies of Islam declared that it owed its success to the sword and not to the power of argument, he summoned a great assembly of the leaders of all the religious bodies of the period. In this meeting, the Muslim doctors defended their religion against the imputation, and the unbelievers acknowledged that the Muslims had satisfactorily proved their point.[86] Prof. Arnold goes on to say: "Al-Mamun himself was very zealous in his efforts to spread the faith of Islam... but he did not abuse his royal power by attempting to force his own faith upon others."[87]

One of the eminent participants in the great inter-religious assembly held in Baghdad, was Yazdanbakht, a leader of the Manichean sect who had come from Persia. He held a disputation with the Muslim theologians, in which he was utterly silenced, so impressed was he by Islam's power of argument. The Caliph then tried to induce him to embrace Islam. But Yazdanbakht refused, saying, "Commander of the Faithful, your advice is heard and your words have been listened to; but you are one of those who do not force men to abandon their religion." Far from resenting the ill-success of his efforts, the Caliph furnished him with armed bodyguards, that he might not be exposed to insult from the fanatical populace.'[88]

Under Islam there is freedom for every thought as well as respect for every thinking man, irrespective of the fact that his thinking may be different from ours. Islam not only grants freedom of thought, but also respects the upholders of all schools of thought.

THE MODERN AGE AND ISLAM

Freedom of thought is held to be the *summum bonum* of the modern age, and is generally thought to be the result of the western scientific revolution. It is true that this is its immediate cause, but the scientific revolution itself (as has been explained in previous chapters) was the result of the Islamic revolution based upon monotheism.

The French philosopher, Jean-Jacques Rousseau (1712-1778), was one of the founders of modern democracy. His book, *The Social Contract,* begins with these words: "Man was born free, but I find him in chains." The sentiment thus expressed—this lamentation over human bondage—is not in actual fact Rousseau's gift to humanity. It is rather an echo of a more splendid utterance of the Islamic Caliph, ʿUmar Ibn-Khattab (586-644), which he made to his governor of Egypt: "O ʿAmr, since when have you enslaved people whose mothers gave birth to them in freedom?" The occasion for this rebuke was the flogging by ʿAmr's son of a young Egyptian who had beaten him in a horse race as recounted above.

The revolution to bring freedom and democracy to the people which began in Europe, later spreading to the rest of the world in modern times, is but the second stage of that revolutionary process which was set in motion in the seventh century by Islam.

THE UNIVERSAL DECLARATION OF HUMAN RIGHTS

Article 18 of Universal Declaration of Human Rights of the United Nations reads as follows:

> Everyone has the right to freedom of thought, conscience and religion; this right includes freedom to change his religion or belief, and freedom, either alone or in community with others and in public or private, to manifest his religion or belief in teaching, practice, worship and observance.

The charter, of which the above article is an extract, is not in actual fact an achievement of the United Nations, but is rather a legacy from that Islamic revolution which was brought into existence a thousand years before the United Nations came into being.

Islam, for the first time in human history, uprooted the system based on polytheism which was responsible for the mentality of discrimination between man and man. This unreal division had been at the root of much of the social injustice which had prevailed in ancient times.

While, on the one hand, Islam changed the human mind, on the other, it brought about a practical revolution on such a vast scale that it ushered in a whole new era of human freedom and human respect. Across the centuries, this revolution went from strength to strength, ultimately bringing Europe under its benign influence. There it culminated in the modern freedom and democracy which nowadays people tend to imagine has existed for all time. But this democratic revolution of modern Europe is but the secular version of the Islamic revolution which was given its first impetus in seventh century Arabia by God's final Prophet.

Seen in this historical perspective, Islam, from the scientific as well as the socio-economic point of view, is the true creator of the modern age.

NOTES

1. Henri Pirenne, *History of Western Europe*.

2. Philip K. Hitti, *History of the Arabs* (London, 1989), p. 4.

3. Ibid., p. 307.

4. Henri Pirenne, *History of Western Europe*.

5. *Encyclopaedia Britannica* (1984), Vol. 4, p. 522.

6. Ibid., Vol. 16, p. 118.

7. J.M. Roberts, *History of the World*, p. 238.

8. *Encyclopaedia Britannica* (1984), Vol. 17, p. 899.

9. *Sahih*, Muslim, Vol. 4.

10. Moseoleban, *The Arab Civilization*.

11. Henri Pirenne, *History of Western Europe*, p. 46.

12. William E. Connolly, *Political Theory and Modernity* (London, 1988).

13. *Encyclopaedia Britannica* (1984), Vol. 4, p. 522.

14. Ibid, Vol. 1, p. 227.

15. Ibid, Vol. 1, p. 479.

16. Ibid, Vol. 3, p. 1084.

17. Philip K. Hitti, *History of the Arabs* (London 1970), p. 166.

18. *The Cambridge History of Islam* (London), Vol. 2-B, p. 888-89.

19. Baron Carra de Vaux, *The Legacy of Islam* (1931).

20. Montgomery Watt, *Majesty That Was Islam* (London), p. 232.

21. Ibid, p. 226.

22. Ibid, p. 226.

23. Ibid, p. 227.

NOTES

24. Ibid, p. 228.

25. Philip K. Hitti, *History of the Arabs* (London, 1970), pp. 575-76.

26. Ibid, p. 380.

27. *Encyclopaedia Britannica* (1984), Vol. 16, p. 367.

28. Ibid, Vol. 16, p. 367.

29. Ibid, Vol. 16, p. 366.

30. Ibid, Vol. 16, p. 366.

31. *The Encyclopaedia of Religion and Ethics* discusses this in detail in its article on "Holiness."

32. *Encyclopaedia Britannica* (1984), Vol. 12, p. 877.

33. Ibid, Vol. 16, p. 124.

34. Ibid, Vol. 16, p. 124.

35. *Statesman* (New Delhi), September 4, 1967.

36. *Indian Express* (New Delhi), September 7, 1967.

37. *Encyclopaedia Britannica* (1984), Vol. III, p. 206.

38. Ibid, Vol. III, p. 380.

39. Bertrand Russell, *History of Western Philosophy*, p. 395.

40. *Encyclopaedia Britannica* (1984), Vol. 15, p. 646.

41. Fred Hoyle, *The Intelligent Universe*, p. 29.

42. Briffault, *Making of Humanity*, p. 190.

43. Ibid, p. 202.

44. *The Encyclopaedia Britannica*, Vol. 15, p. 646.

45. Philip K. Hitti, *History of the Arabs* (London, 1970), p. 307.

46. Bertrand Russell, *The Impact of Science on Society*, p. 29.

47. Ibid, p. 17.

48. Arnold J. Toynbee quoted in *Reader's Digest*, March 1974.

49. *Encyclopaedia Britannica* (1984), Vol. 14, p. 385.

50. *Encyclopaedia Britannica* (1984), Vol. 18, p. 1013.

51. Edward Mc Nall Burns, *Western Civilization* (New York, 1955), p. 36.

52. *Encyclopaedia Britannica* (1984), Vol. 8, pp. 942-43.

53. Ibid, Vol. 7, p. 850.

54. Ibid, Vol. 9, p. 280.

55. William L. Wonderly and Eugene Nida in *Linguistics and Christian Missions, Anthropological Linguistics*, Vol. 5, pp. 104-144.

56. Philip K. Hitti, *History of the Arabs* (London, 1970) p. 573.

57. Wilfrid Blunt, quoted in *The Times* (London), April 2, 1976.

58. *The Times of India* (New Delhi), January 30, 1989, p. 6.

59. Dilip M. Salwai, *Story of Zero* (New Delhi).

60. *Encyclopaedia Britannica* (1984), Vol. 1, p. 469.

61. Ibid, Vol. 10, p. 817.

62. Bertrand Russell, *A History of Western Society* (London, 1984), p. 416.

63. *Encyclopaedia Britannica* (1984), Vol. 1, p. 1175.

64. Ibid, Vol. 17, p. 129.

65. Ibid, Vol. 12, p. 882.

66. Philip K. Hitti, *History of the Arabs* (London, 1970), p. 528.

67. Bertrand Russell, *A History of Western Philosophy*, p. 416.

68. *Encyclopaedia Britannica* (1984), Vol. X, p. 76.

69. Ibid, Vol. 9, p. 148.

70. Philip K. Hitti, *History of the Arabs* (London, 1970), p. 568.

71. *Encyclopaedia Britannica* (1984), Vol. 9, p. 147.

72. Ibid, Vol. V, p. 816.

73. *Mishkat al-Masabih,* Chapter entitled *Salat al-Khushuᶜ.*

74. *Muslim Rulers,* p. 415, with reference to *Nafh al Tayyib,* Part I, pp. 362-368.

75. *Encyclopaedia Britannica* (1984), Vol. 8, p. 782.

76. *Letters of Swami Vivekanand.*

77. Hadīth of Bukhārī.

78. *Encyclopaedia Britannica* (1984), Vol. 9, p. 144.

79. Ibid, Vol. III, p. 1083.

NOTES

80. Ibid, Vol. III, p. 1084.
81. Ibid, Vol. III, p. 1084.
82. Ibid, Vol. III, p. 1085.
83. T.W. Arnold, *The Preaching of Islam*, p. 143.
84. Ibid, p. 157.
85. Ibid, p. 158-59.
86. Ibid, p. 86.
87. Ibid, p. 86.
88. Ibid, p. 85.